LAST OF THE
SUMMER WINE

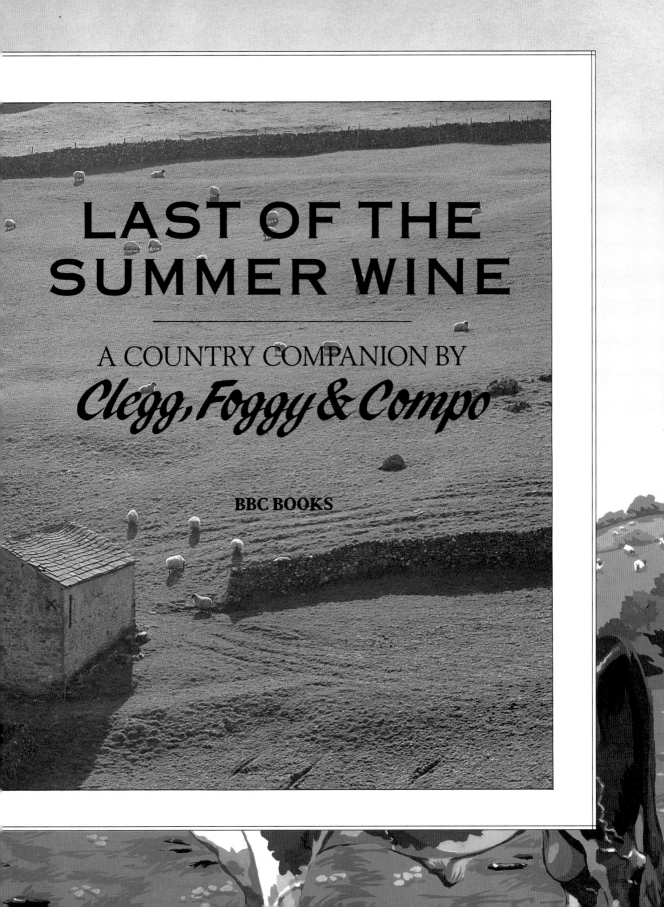

LAST OF THE SUMMER WINE

A COUNTRY COMPANION BY

Clegg, Foggy & Compo

BBC BOOKS

Published by BBC Books,
a division of BBC Enterprises Limited,
Woodlands, 80 Wood Lane
London W12 0TT

First Published 1992

Last of the Summer Wine format and television scripts
© Roy Clarke 1992. This book © Paul Ableman.

ISBN 0 563 36480 7

Designed by Hammond Hammond
Illustrations by Chris Lloyd, Larry Rostant,
Hussein Hussein

Set in Plantin by Goodfellow & Egan Ltd, Cambridge
Printed and bound in Great Britain by
Butler & Tanner Ltd, Frome.
Colour separation by Dot Gradations Chelmsford.
Jacket printed by Lawrence Allen, Weston-Super-Mare.

CONTENTS

LAST OF THE SUMMER WINE

INTRODUCTION

What, another book about the Yorkshire Moors? Indeed yes, but one which is as unique as it is delightful. To make good that claim, I can hardly do better than recount to you the astonishing circumstances in which it came to be written. For the three men who are both its heroes and its creators are not, amazingly, professional authors at all and would never have produced this astounding work but for a chance meeting which seemed initially like a disaster but proved ultimately a blessing for all concerned.

It happened just three years ago when a close friend and I, longtime enthusiasts of Moorland, were spending a short holiday in that glorious part of England. Driving across a lonely stretch of moor, and mercifully travelling quite slowly so as to miss none of the superb scenery, we were both startled to perceive someone or something leap out of the roadside bushes and rush into the path of our car. Almost immediately we felt a sickening thud as the vehicle struck something solid.

Naturally, I braked at once and, with a terrible sense of foreboding, climbed out of the car and gazed back the way we had come. My worst fears appeared to have been justified when I saw, just a few yards behind the car, a sprawled figure lying motionless in the road. I hastened towards it and soon saw that it was, in fact, a small, scruffy man whom, from the extreme dilapidation of his clothing, I assumed to be a tramp. Fearing the worst I knelt beside this pathetic apparition, whereupon it opened one eye and remarked:

'Hey up, lucky you only clouted me on the head or you might have done some real damage.'

'Why did you run under my car?' I demanded, with a mixture of reproach and relief now that I perceived that my 'victim' was not too severely injured.

'I didn't. I was trying to escape from Foggy and Clegg. The daft clowns only wanted me to jump off Beacon Point using a pair of Nora Batty's old bloomers as a parachute.'

Naturally, I could make small sense of this. The scruffy little man now heaved himself into a sitting posture and said: 'You're not from round here. I can tell by your plummy accent.'

I explained that we were from London. A thoughtful look came into his eye and he asked, 'Are you one of them yuppies? If you are you could stand me a pint to help me get over this terrible accident.'

I told him that I was by profession a publisher but that I would, of course, be happy to stand him a pint. He stared at me hard and said: 'A publisher? That's summat to do wi' books, innit?'

I agreed that it was, whereupon he climbed unsteadily to his feet and staggered about for a little while. He then asked me, 'Well then, if I wrote you a book might there be a few bob in it for me?'

To humour the fellow, for his actions made me fear that he might in fact have suffered a skull fracture after all, I agreed that authors are normally paid for their work.

He nodded and said ruefully: 'Trouble is, I don't know how to write books. But Cleggy does. Leastways he probably does because he can talk quite posh when he wants to. If you give me your address, I'll get him to write you a book and send it to you.'

'Excellent idea,' I said soothingly, and I took my wallet from my breast pocket and withdrew one of my cards from it. 'Here's my address, but now I want you to get into my car so that I can run you to the nearest hospital for a check-up.'

I then saw that Compo, which I now know is the name of the short fellow, was gazing over my shoulder with an anxious expression.

'Hey up,' he cried. 'Here they come again.'

I turned and immediately saw two taller men leaping across the moors towards us waving, like a battle standard, a large pair of bloomers.

'Can't hang about,' explained Compo, with which words he started away like a hare. But he had only covered a few yards when he did an about-turn, darted back to me, seized the card from my hand and once more shot away.

An instant later, the two taller men, with polite nods and greetings, also passed us, travelling at speed. My friend and I watched the trio disappearing into the valley and then, still rather shaken, we climbed back into our car and resumed our journey.

Over the next few months, under the pressure of a busy social and professional life, the incident naturally faded from memory. I was therefore initially mystified when, rather more than a year later, an unsolicited manuscript turned up in our offices accompanied by a note written in a semi-literate hand on the back of a grimy old milk bill. It read:

TOLD YOU CLEGGY COULD RITE A BOOK IF HE TRIED. NATCHERLY I HAVENT RID IT SEPT FOR THE BITS WHAT I ROTE BUT I BET ITS A LOT BITTER THAN MOST OF THE STUFF YOU PUBLISH. PLEASE SEND THE MONEY TO ME, COMPO, AT THE ADDRESS ON TUTHER SIDE OV THIS LITTER AND ILL GIVE TUTHERS THIR SHEER.

Even then, it was not until I began curiously turning through the manuscript and discovering that it was a guide or companion to West Yorkshire that I suddenly recalled my near-disastrous encounter with the scruffy little man on the moorland road and realised who 'Compo' must be. Although extremely sceptical about the value of any work with which the fellow might have been connected, I felt that I owed him at least a 'publisher's reading' (a glance at every fourth or fifth page) and I therefore took the book home with me that evening.

Suffice it to say that the first glance kept my eyes firmly fixed to the page and I did not rise from my chair until, stiff and weary but also filled with the excitement of discovery, I reached the end of the book in the small hours.

And now, a year later, with the addition of illustrations, maps, drawings and photographs which were beyond Clegg's simple resources, I have enormous pleasure in setting before you, the reader, one of the most original and amusing books on the English countryside it has ever been my good fortune to publish. There is no need to say more. The book says it all.

CHRIS WELLER

COUNTRY MOOCHING

I've never written a book before and I'm not at all sure why I'm writing one now. It might have something to do with the fact that Compo encountered a publisher the other day up on the Beacon Road. So eager was this publisher, according to Compo, to secure his literary services that he knocked Compo down with his car to prevent him getting away. Then he practically begged Compo to write him a book. It was only later, when he was tucked up in bed with his ferrets, that it occurred to Compo that his writing ability was quite adequate for signing his monthly dole cheque receipt but not much more. He thereupon concluded that I would have to write the book. But why, you may well ask, should either of us write a book? Well, for Compo the answer to that one is easy. There could, he reckons, be a bob or two in it. My own view is that Compo would stand a better chance of one day being in a position to buy a round of drinks by panning for gold in Scanders Brook. In that case, why am I embarking on such a mammoth task? Would you think I was crazy if I said I had no idea? Yes, you probably would. But the fact is I always welcome a challenge, as long as it has nothing to do with sport. Then again, apart from a little light boozing, a lot of heavy mooching and occasionally rolling Compo down a hill when I feel the need for really rib-tickling entertainment, I have few occupations these days. Writing a book might just be what I need to give a sense of direction to my life. So naturally I felt I ought to try it and find out.

Since I spend more time mooching than doing anything else, I felt it would be appropriate to begin this book with a chapter on it. But that immediately raises the question: What is mooching? How, in fact, does one actually mooch? I know. You think I should look the word up in a dictionary. The trouble is I have a rooted objection to looking up words in dictionaries. It

OFF FOR A DAY'S MOOCHING.

is, in my opinion, bad for them. I have even known words keel over and die just from being looked up in dictionaries. So I have decided to kick off straightforwardly with an example of Grade A, 21-carat, copper-bottomed mooching by Compo, Foggy and myself. We will take as our specimen mooch last Tuesday morning, when Foggy and I called round on Compo to see if he was in the mood for being thrown over a wall. He said, no, it was more, in his opinion, the kind of day for falling into a stream but he agreed to accompany us none the less.

We set off in no particular direction – and this indicates a very important rule of mooching. It is absolutely indispensable to have no good reason for going anywhere. As soon as things like motivation and destination come into the picture mooching flies out. Your truly dedicated moocher will do enterprising things like getting up in the middle of the night and walking three times round the village green just to demonstrate how free he is from any taint of necessity. Indeed, I heard of a moocher once – up near the Lancashire border – who, in his lifelong pursuit of better and purer mooching, put on a dinner-jacket one sunny morning, lit a large cigar and strolled over a cliff. There is a handsome memorial commemorating this supreme mooching achievement. For most of us, however, this is carrying the art to excess. It is enough that we are free, when we set out in the morning, from any taint of purpose and that is the condition in which, nineteen times out of twenty, Compo, Foggy and I will embark on a jolly day's mooch.

Well, on this occasion, we mooched through a few streets and into the library just in time to see the librarian, Mr Wainright, laying licentious hands on the assistant librarian, Mrs Partridge. These two have been having a very on and off affair for some years now and appear to believe that no one has

COUNTRY MOOCHING

BIKE MOOCHING IS FUN TOO.

noticed. Since their amorous activities constitute one of the chief sources of entertainment and conversation for the whole town, and not least for their spouses, I have sometimes felt that it would be a kindness to inform them that their secret is out. But then I have reflected that, quite possibly, it is the sense of romance they derive from indulging in what they believe to be a clandestine passion which is their chief source of pleasure in the relationship and so I have refrained.

As soon as we entered, Mr Wainright ceased hugging Mrs Partridge and pretended he had merely been attempting to reach a volume inconveniently placed behind her. We continued past his desk to the newspaper annexe where Compo began studying a racing page and eating one of his mighty sandwiches. He remarked, with mouth full: 'They're still at it, I see.'

Foggy said to him sternly, 'You can't eat that in here. What if Mr Wainright comes in?'

Compo, spattering Foggy with chewed bread and cheese, urged reassuringly, 'He won't. He'll be too busy thumbing through Mrs Partridge.'

I said wistfully, 'Many years ago, before I was intimate with Muriel Fairfax –'

'Were you?' asked Compo thickly.

'In a manner of speaking. One Tuesday. In their sand-pit.'

'Her from Finkle Street?'

'Yes.'

'How do you mean – in a manner of speaking?'

'She let me see her without her vest – which I always felt constituted a bond between us. Though it didn't stop her marrying that bread man.'

Foggy asked, 'How old were you then?'

'Nine or ten. But it was one of those formative experiences you don't forget.'

I was about to develop this theme when Mr Wainright appeared at the door, turned purple at seeing Compo devouring what looked like the entire EEC bread mountain and ordered us from his establishment.

After this, we found our way to Syd's café, and after that down four streets, across three fields, up a considerable hill and so on to the banks of a very pretty stream. It was there that we resumed talking about sex. It should be clear to you, the reader, by now that mooching conversation obeys much the same laws as mooching itself. It should never be concerned with what you are actually doing. No moocher worth his salt would say: 'I think I felt a drop of rain just then. Shall we continue on to East Boltham or go back by the Pollingham Road?'

FIRST LOVE

I once loved Muriel Fairfax
And life was then quite sweet
Because you see my love and I
Did every evening meet.

It was not in the garden
Nor bedroom dimly lit
No she and I had our affair
In her family sandpit.

For she was only eight, I fear,
And I was not yet ten
And the wilder shores of romance
Were quite beyond our ken.

And yet we built our castles
Which often were quite grand
Not castles in the air of course
But only in the sand.

And though we were but children
We promised we'd be true
And never play at houses
With anybody new.

And just to prove she loved me
Right there in our sandy nest
One summer day she showed me
Herself without her vest.

She didn't look much different
From me without the same
But somehow then I realised
She'd always be my flame.

But that was very long ago
And Muriel's long since sped
Into the arms of a fellow
That delivers lots of bread.

And yet I know most surely
That till the day I die
The thought of Muriel Fairfax
Will wring from me a sigh.

Oh, I have since been wedded
And known a few girls more
But yearn still for my first love
On that distant, sandy shore.

A SMILING WELCOME AT SYD'S CAFE.

No, that would be utterly alien to the spirit of mooching. It would be quite in order to say 'Air travel is cheap in Russia' or 'Personally I have no belief in original sin but how else can one explain Compo?'. On this occasion, it was actually Compo himself who wistfully asked Foggy, 'Does tha reckon I'm in love wi' Nora Batty or is it just sex?'

'Love?' asked Foggy with a dazed expression. 'What do you know of love?'

'Why shouldn't he know about love?' I asked gleefully, more to encourage Foggy than to support Compo.

Foggy shook his head and enquired sadly, 'Him? Do you know how he started his romantic career? Stuffing broken biscuits down Olive Sanderson's knickers.'

'True,' admitted Compo. 'But that were research. I wanted to see if it were true, what Doggy Mason had said.'

'And what had Doggy Mason said?' I asked.

'He reckoned she'd have a trap-door.'

'A trap-door!' exclaimed Foggy incredulously.

Compo nodded glumly.

'Aye. He said that's how babbies were born.'

'Through a trap-door!' repeated Foggy, with popping eyes.

But this seemed to me excessive disbelief.

'Think of it, Foggy,' I urged. 'Is it any weirder than the truth?'

A veteran moocher, Foggy dropped the topic and simply remarked, 'I understand the Co-op has some big reductions in winceyette pyjamas.'

To demonstrate that I was every bit his equal in spurning the point, I observed, 'I could do with some big reductions in mine. I think they must have been made for a gorilla. Perhaps only a small gorilla.'

Compo announced magisterially, 'Nigel Hinchcliffe's nose has gone septic.'

It is not, of course, compulsory for moochers to ignore the previous remark. Not at all. Some of the most exhaustive, well exhausting, conversations I have ever had have been while mooching with Foggy and Compo. It is just a case of some subjects catching on and others failing to do so. Nigel Hinchcliffe's nose proved to be a winner.

'All of it?' I asked interestedly. 'Or just the bit that sticks out?'

Compo said stiffly, 'That's all there is to a nose. The bit that sticks out.'

'Not necessarily,' I objected. 'Not if it's like an iceberg. If it is like an iceberg it could mean that nine-tenths of the human nose is under the surface and the bridge, which is the bit that sticks out, is just for resting your spectacles on.'

We had, while pursuing this fascinating topic, been toiling up a hairpin path leading to one of the highest peaks in the district. Now we reached it and paused, as a single moocher, to gaze panting at the majestic prospect.

Foggy, deviating a little from moochers' cool, gasped, 'Is that a view or is that a view?'

'You mean you don't know?' I protested.

Foggy ignored my ironic query.

'On a clear day,' he proclaimed, 'you can see the Humber Bridge.'

'Wi'its spectacles on?' asked Compo.

Foggy beat him lightly about the head with his hat inducing Compo to protest loudly. And so the day proceeded pleasantly enough until, about mid-afternoon, we found ourselves strolling along a narrow road in the vague direction of

THE HARD CLIMB TO THE SUMMIT.

17

home. It was then that we saw the car.

There was a woman inside it and a man outside it. The bonnet was raised suggesting that the car was not in an operational mode. Although we were crossing a field on a path that ran parallel to the road, and about a hundred yards away from him, we could see that the man was waving his arms above his head as if signalling to us.

'That man's waving at us,' pronounced Foggy.

'Do you think we ought to wave back?' I asked uncertainly. 'I like to be neighbourly.'

'I think we ought to ignore him,' said Compo stoutly.

'Actually, he's not waving at us,' Foggy corrected himself. 'He's appealing for help.'

'Then we should definitely ignore him,' insisted Compo.

Foggy was outraged.

'Ignore him?' he remonstrated. 'A man in distress? And a woman too? Have you no chivalry?'

'No,' said Compo rummaging in his pockets. 'It must be in me other trousers. And it's no good for mending cars anyhow.'

'Follow me!' ordered Foggy and set off at rapid march towards the stranded vehicle.

I suppose it was inevitable that, quarter of an hour later, we found ourselves pushing the car, which was one of those hefty aristocratic models top people favour, up a remarkably steep hill. The man proved to be a decent sort and gave us a hand, managing to steer through the open door, but his lady wife kept urging irritably, 'Do hurry up, Clarence. I promised the Lord-Lieutenant we'd be there for the opening.'

I had already noticed that they were both very elegantly attired and so this reference to the mighty one of the district did not surprise me.

'It might help, Melissa, if you got out of the car,' urged the man.

'It is not my sphere to trail my Hardy Amies tea gown in the dust of the road,' returned the haughty lady. 'It is my sphere to shine at glittering occasions.'

At this, her husband, earning my undying respect, muttered under his breath, but loudly enough for me, toiling immediately behind him, to hear: 'Oh, spheres to you.'

He further endeared himself to me, and even more to Compo, by dipping into his wallet, once we'd reached the top, and fishing out a tenner which he handed gratefully to Foggy with the words, 'Well done, chaps. One more little push and I'll be able to start her on the roll.'

'Right. Heave!' ordered Foggy.

'Hey up. Me trousers are caught!' protested Compo.

But he was too late.

The car began to roll, slowly at first but with gathering speed, down the long slope ahead. And it was then that I saw that a woollen thread connected its bumper with Compo's tattered and, as always, disgraceful trousers.

'Never mind,' I reassured him. 'It'll snap in a moment.'

But Compo's nether garment proved to have good stuff in it. Possibly before descending to him, doubtless through a long line of scarecrows, it had originally been constructed out of the best Hebridean wool. In any event, it now demonstrated its noble ancestry. So far from snapping as the Mercedes disappeared into the distance, it trailed after the aristocratic vehicle and naturally, by doing so, deprived Compo of its companionship. Foggy and I watched in appalled dismay as larger and larger portions of Compo's lower

THE BATTYS OUT FOR A SPIN IN THEIR ELEGANT EQUIPAGE.

anatomy became available to the public gaze. Hardly more than a minute had passed before he stood before us in the middle of the road clad only in quite unspeakable undergarments.

'Over the wall, quickly,' urged Foggy, gazing anxiously about lest anyone appear to see the horrid spectacle. 'If a nervous spinster should happen past we could have blood on our hands.'

'I'm not walking over there on the – ' began Compo firmly, but we never discovered what his objections to the cow field beyond the wall were. At that very moment, there came from behind us the unmistakable hoarse roar of

COMPO'S CAPABLE CLOTHES
The Ideal Outfit For Out Of Doors

Warm woollen CAP with reinforced brow-band to ward off the 'wind on the heath' and possible attacks by enraged women.

CRAVAT which in rural circumstances can easily double as a handkerchief or even napkin.

Striped SWEATER of nondescript appearance. This garment complements superbly the cravat and cap to produce that fashionable 'scarecrow' look.

SHIRT. Note lack of collar which assists freedom of movement when, for example, ferreting or mooching.

Superb bell-shaped JACKET with deep pockets. The ergonomic design supports the body flexibly and comfortably during the many demands made on it by country living. Whether your busy daily round includes being rolled down a hill or fleeing enraged women, the jacket ensures ample freedom of movement to cope with the physical stresses involved.

STRING USED AS BELT. A simple and effective adaptation which, to the discriminating eye, is much more attractive than the conventional, boring leather strap.

Dark TROUSERS of jaunty 'jodhpur' cut. The garment is designed to accommodate up to seven ferrets in the greatest possible comfort.

The outfit is completed by warm, no-nonsense, woollen UNDERWEAR and thick SOCKS. These intimate items will benefit from a good annual wash with some standard soap or detergent.

Tough black WELLIES (none of your trendy, but lightweight, green ones). Note the many holes strategically located to enable water to run out after wearer's possible immersion in a stream or pond.

Forget flimsy designer garments. Here is country fashion as worn by a true countryman and tailored to last a lifetime.

a motor cycle. Foggy and I moved as one defender of public decency. After a brief tussle between us to secure the head end, which mercifully I won, we seized Compo firmly and heaved him unceremoniously over the wall. None too soon. A motor-cycle combination of venerable years, and which we recognised from a distance as the property of Wally Batty, thrummed past at the speed of a galloping tortoise. Planted gravely in its open side-car, and looking as solemn as Queen Victoria if not quite as regal, sat Nora Batty. The speed, or lack of it, of the vehicle gave plenty of time for Wally to touch his cap as it drummed past and call, 'Arternoon.'

'Afternoon Wally,' called Foggy.

'Afternoon Nora,' I added, which won from the lady merely a stony stare.

There came a wail of anguish from behind the wall.

'My Norah! Is she here? Norah, wait for me, lass. I must at least blow thee a kiss.'

But disaster had mercifully been averted. By the time Compo, looking like a hideous travesty of some classical painting called 'Thwarted Passion' or something similar, had scrambled on to the wall and was gazing mournfully after the retreating vehicle, the Battys had passed beyond the danger area. So we threw Compo back over the wall and wouldn't let him join us again until he had found something, an old zinc wash-basin actually, with which to hide his partial, but still appalling, nakedness. And after that we just mooched on home.

So there you have it. Mooching in the raw. I do hope you enjoyed my account of it because, willy-nilly, there's bound to be quite a bit of the activity in this book. We think it's wonderful. And you never know what surprises it can spring. For example, do you recall what Compo said when we first called for him that morning? He said that in his opinion it wasn't the kind of day for being thrown over a wall but the kind of day for falling into a stream. Well, he proved to be quite wrong, didn't he? Makes you think, doesn't it? And if it doesn't, you can take comfort from the thought that there's probably far too much thinking in the world in any case. And not nearly enough mooching. We're just trying to redress the balance a little.

COUNTRY PURSUITS

No, this is not meant to be a chapter about Compo's love life. We have had enough of that unedifying saga already. It is, rather, a section on the many attractive activities which can only, or at least chiefly, be enjoyed in a rural setting. But, you may be wondering, are we three really the best guides to country pursuits since, as I have often stressed, we are essentially moochers who eschew (one of my all-time favourite words) activities that require planning and equipment. Perhaps, at this point, I should concede that it is me that does most of the eschewing. Foggy, on the other hand, does sometimes develop a craze on some activity. His crazes are almost invariably financial in origin. He becomes convinced that there is a fortune to be made out of some occupation like walking dogs or metal detecting. The latter, incidentally, is an incredibly boring activity, a little like vacuum-cleaning the planet. Three long days of it left Foggy in possession of one of the finest collection of rusty tins in West Yorkshire but very little else.

In fairness, however, it must be conceded that it is Compo rather than Foggy who is most often afflicted with a desire to take up some accepted sport or hobby. This has sometimes made me wonder if Compo can really be considered a deep-down, single-minded, bred-in-the-bone moocher at all. But then he surprises me by going for weeks, or even months, without manifesting any desire to drive a hot-rod or carve Beacon Hill into an immense likeness of Nora Batty. Yes, it must be admitted that for most of the time he easily outclasses Foggy and me in mooching, practising it so devotedly that if came to deciding which was the most successful moocher, Compo or your average stray dog, it would be hard to come down in the dog's favour.

For all that, the three of us have, over the years, on one occasion or another, practised a wide range of country pursuits, and our experience can hardly be ignored in the present work. Some of these pursuits are probably too simple, and indeed childish, to appeal to the class of visitor we expect to get in these parts. I mean a jet-setting executive and his family, spending a week at a four-star hotel in some celebrated beauty spot and viewing the glories of the countryside exclusively through the windows of a stretched limousine (and even if no cruelty is involved why can't they just build these cars longer rather than having to stretch the poor things?), are unlikely to be much attracted by the homely diversion of Foot Guessing.

This pursuit was, in fact, our own invention. Admittedly, we did not sit down with a drawing-board and a range of coloured pencils to devise it. It came about, like most of our activities, pretty much by chance. We were out mooching one day and just happened to pass, in a farmyard, a car that was jacked up on blocks and which had someone at work beneath it. All you could see of the person under the car was a pair of feet sticking out. Nevertheless, Compo called cheerfully, 'How do, Charlie.'

Foggy immediately remonstrated, 'That wasn't Charlie. That was Eric.'

Compo laughed derisively.

'Little tha knows,' he exclaimed. 'Eric's just run off to Wales with Sophie from the railway buffet.'

'I'm sure it was Eric,' protested Foggy. 'I'd recognise his ankles anywhere.'

So naturally there was nothing for it but to go back and find out. We all crouched down and gazed under the horrible old banger. The mechanic turned out to be a stranger: a brawny young fellow with sideburns who, assuming we were taking the mickey, snarled and brandished a big spanner in

A HIDEOUS, CLAPPED-OUT OLD BANGER.

our direction. We ran away glancing fearfully back over our shoulders. But the young bully contented himself with throwing a handful of dust after us. And that is how foot guessing was born.

All over the Stonefirth area one sees hideous, clapped-out old cars jacked up on blocks, and quite often you will also see, as you mooch past, feet sticking out from under them. As a result the three of us now have a regular challenge whereby we all have a go at guessing whose feet they are. The one, if any, that gets it right doesn't have to buy a round that day.

Compo has become such an expert at foot guessing that Foggy and I are convinced that he has secretly photographed all the male feet for miles around and studies them for a hour or so every evening, but we have never caught him at it. Still, as regards this chapter, let us concede that foot guessing is not really a true-blue country pursuit but only a moochers' pastime and, as such, is unlikely to be of much interest to the executive in the stretched limousine.

What the executive is quite certain to be keen on is the country pursuit that cropped up in a conversation at Syd and Ivy's a couple of years back.

Foggy said, 'It's a crude, unpolished game. It lacks finesse. It's very much the rough, knockabout sport of the working classes.'

No, no, don't adjust your sets. That was just the lead-in.

Syd, looking puzzled, asked, 'What's he on about?'

I replied, 'The rough knockabout sport of the working classes. You know – the one with the tight blonde hair that lives in Gregson Street.'

'Oh,' exclaimed Syd, as enlightenment dawned. 'You mean Trudy Edwards?' He nodded thoughtfully and went on, 'The last I heard she'd been going out wi' little Tommy Weston, but I understand he's recovering nicely in hospital.'

Foggy here interrupted irritably.

THE LATEST FAD: BICYCLE POLO.

'No, no, I meant that the game of football is intrinsically crude.'

Syd looked appalled at this sacrilege.

'It's pure poetry,' he exclaimed.

'Rubbish,' said Foggy haughtily.

'What's your idea of a good game then?' asked Syd curiously.

Foggy smiled silkily and replied, 'Golf.'

Which is, of course, what I've been leading up to all along. Golf. The country holiday within a country holiday. The high flyer's favourite frivolity. The yuppies' delight. The executive's entertainment. The game of grandees.

But you might not have appreciated this if your only experience of the sport was watching Foggy during that long afternoon we spent on the links soon after the above conversation. It started badly with Foggy discovering that his old clubs, which had been stored in his attic and which he hadn't inspected for years, had become warped with age. Indeed, so far out of true were they that Compo suggested we might do better to try and flog them as a set of high-tech gardening tools or even as modernistic corkscrews, but Foggy decided that he'd get a visitor's ticket for the local golf club just to see if it was still possible to play a round with them.

The round proved to be rare entertainment despite, or perhaps because of, the fact that it only remotely resembled golf. Foggy would address the ball, gaze earnestly down the fairway and swing with a nice wrist movement, whereupon his club would lurch crazily through the air rather like a whiz-bang on Guy Fawkes night. If it did happen to connect with the ball

FOGGY'S OWN KIND OF CRAZY GOLF.

the result was more like roulette than honest sport. You could have taken bets on which way the ball would actually travel. Since it took Foggy some twenty or thirty strokes to connect, every time he attempted a shot he naturally generated a good deal of animosity from fellow golfers who were awaiting their turn at the tees. The first time this occurred an impatient golfer who looked, as so many golfers seem to look, like a retired colonel, finally abandoned the tee to Foggy and stalked off in the direction of the second green. Foggy noticed that he had left two golf balls behind and called politely after him.

'You've left your golf balls, sir.'

The colonel was already quite a long way away and only just caught the message. He turned and called back, 'What?'

Foggy shouted as loudly as he could, 'Balls, sir.'

You could almost see the other swelling with rage as he cupped his hands over his mouth and then, in a voice that must have thundered over many a parade ground, bellowed back.

'And the same to you, sir.'

Foggy was quite distressed and said to us, 'Oh dear, now someone unscrupulous may find them and sell them to the club shop.'

'What does tha mean?' asked Compo.

'The club shop pays threepence for any balls that players find. It then sells them for a shilling,' Foggy explained.

'Tha don't say,' exclaimed Compo avariciously, stooping to pick up the abandoned balls.

'Don't you dare touch those,' ordered Foggy. 'The player may still come back for them and I'm not having him think we're thieves.'

After that Foggy gamely continued what was really a round of crazy golf played on a real golf course. About half-way through it I noticed that Compo had disappeared and assumed he was prospecting for rabbits. He had earlier remarked that it looked like a good place for them. But it turned out my assumption was wrong. Hours later, as the sun was setting and we finally reached the last green, the reason for Compo's earlier disappearance became clear. To Foggy's horror and my amusement, there the little man stood with a tray, like that of an ice cream girl in a cinema, strapped to his chest. On the tray were thirty or forty golf balls that he must have found in the roughs. Pinned untidily to Compo's chest was a crudely written sign which read:

BARGAIN BALLS. HALF AS MUCH AND TWICE AS GOOD AS THA WILL FIND AT THE CLUB SHOP. JUST FIVE SHILLINGS EACH. OR THREE FOR TEN BOB.

He told us later he'd made quite a handsome profit on the day's sport.

Of course, the ultimate country pursuit has to be camping, but I very much fear that we three cannot be of much help to you on that subject. Living permanently in the countryside we have never felt it necessary to camp out in it. Our own homes and beds are usually damp and cold enough to satisfy even the most masochistic craving for nature in the raw.

Actually, I don't believe Foggy or Compo have ever spent a night under canvas in their entire lives. Well, perhaps Foggy has, when he was in the army, although my guess is that a Nissen hut at Aldershot is the closest he ever really came to roughing it. So probably my own modest experience is the sum total of our team wisdom on the activity. Just how modest my experience really is can best be revealed by setting down a conversation Compo and I had with Cyril Blamire, in the old days before Foggy came to strew wisdom in our path.

I had been entertaining Cyril and Compo at my place and, opening a cupboard to get out my tea things, exposed something within that interested Cyril. He pointed and remarked, 'What's the tent for, Clegg? I don't remember you ever going camping.'

I looked at the thing and realised that I must have looked at it every day for years but had long ago given up actually seeing it. It had become just a well-mannered tent that lived in my cupboard and was so quiet in its ways that I had quite forgotten that we shared a home.

I smiled and said, 'We only used it once. My wife and I. It took me months to talk her into trying it and then one single night in the open was all we ever had.'

Cyril, a very suave and sophisticated man, frowned in slight bafflement.

COMPO WILL DO ANYTHING TO GET HIS HANDS ON NORA BATTY — BUT WHY DOES HE SUPPOSE SHE'LL FANCY HIM AS A TRANSCORSETITE?

'But why did you want to camp? I've always regarded it as only slightly less disagreeable than death by drowning.'

'Which it resembles somewhat,' I observed. 'But the reason for my enthusiasm at the time was that I'd just read *The Last of the Mohicans* and was completely under the book's spell. I was desperate to practise woodcraft.'

Compo stopped ferreting about in his trousers for some purpose which neither Cyril nor I wished to speculate upon. He asked interestedly, 'What did your wife make of it?'

'Nothing very positive,' I had to confess. 'Well, you know how it is. Very few mature married women really enjoy playing Indians.'

Cyril cast a baleful eye on Compo, who had resumed ferreting in his trousers but was now also making sudden swift excursions in the direction of his armpits, and said feelingly.

'Oh, I don't know. I have an idea that Nora Batty might really enjoy scalping itchy trousers here.'

'I can't find me ferret,' explained Compo. 'No, wait a minute. I left the little beggar at home. He were sick in the night. But what were that about Nora Batty? She fancies me, tha knows.'

'In that case, she's a genius at hiding her feelings,' observed Cyril.

'It's just that she's got to be very careful. She's a married woman and Wally is capable of fearful storms of jealousy.'

'Wally?' I asked incredulously.

'Aye, when Desmond the Tinman got an Algerian plum – that's a pigeon tha knows – Wally were so jealous 'e went round and grumbled at him.'

'That must have struck terror into Desmond's soul,' I conceded. 'But all this Women's Lib – it's never really going to make them like us, is it? Not until they can fall in love with railway engines and postage stamps and – well, pigeons and ferrets.'

'No sane man could fall in love with a pigeon,' maintained Compo.

'Where did you go for your Wild West adventure?' Cyril asked me.

'We only had this one night in a field. It was just off the East Lancs Road. My wife insisted on maintaining a lifeline to all the public amenities. There was me, thinking in terms of uncharted wilderness, and early in the morning a fellow comes into our field and dumps an old mattress and the innards of a slot machine next to the tent.'

'My God, there are some heathens about!' exclaimed Cyril feelingly.

Compo echoed him.

'There are and all. Dumping stuff like that. It would certainly have fetched a few bob as scrap.'

'And you've never used the tent since?' asked Cyril, glancing at Compo incredulously.

'No. The wife just wasn't at home in a field. While I was putting up the tent and trying to make things snug she just sat there in her best navy coat and chapel hat, obviously pining for her draining board. I pointed out a passing curlew and a huge tear began to trickle down her cheek. And the next day, when I'd struck camp, she wept all the way home, just breaking off occasionally to give me roasting hell for expecting her to eat baked beans with a spoon. As soon as we got home she drank two cups of scalding hot tea and then papered a ceiling. And I packed the tent away in this cupboard and – I'm pretty sure I've never touched it since.'

But although Compo, Foggy and I may be poor guides to camping, we do have a certain amount of expertise in the modern, high-tech, very chic and much respected country pursuit of hang-gliding. This is because Compo has

THE ICARUS OF OUR AGE!

several times enlisted Foggy and me as helpers for serious attempts on the record. As regards his first two tries, we never found out exactly which record he was making a serious attempt on. But that scarcely mattered because he did not, in any case, have a proper hang-glider and the cardboard wings he was using hardly even softened his fall when he plummeted off barn roofs. His third attempt, however, was a very dedicated affair. He was seeking to wrest the 'twice round the reservoir' distance record from a local title-holder and using a superb, pigeon-based hang-glider designed and built for him by Wally Batty.

While we were waiting for Compo, who was making last-minute preparations behind the hangar (the same old barn we'd used in previous attempts), Foggy explained to me.

'I can't quite recall the mathematical formula, but basically it's a question of providing him with sufficient forward momentum.'

'Let me ask you a non-technical question, Foggy,' I requested. 'Will it be dangerous?'

IS IT A BIRD? IS IT A PLANE?

34

Foggy laughed at my trepidation.

'Dangerous? Good heavens, no. Why should there be any danger? He's the one that's going up in the air.'

I tried to clarify my meaning.

'No, what I meant, Foggy, is there going to be any danger for him?'

'Oh, for him?' Foggy frowned at this novel idea. 'Well, I don't suppose so, no. I mean, it's difficult to wipe out his sort. One thing there's never a shortage of is unemployed scruffy little layabouts. And then you must remember that I'm taking all reasonable precautions.'

'I see. How high do you think he'll go?'

'Well, quite frankly, in that home-made hang-glider Wally's knocked together for him, I think he's going to be lucky if we can get him any higher than fifty feet.'

I gulped.

'Fifty feet, eh? How lucky can you get.'

Foggy turned and called in the direction of the barn.

'Well, come on then. If you're coming.'

'I'm coming. I'm coming.'

And sure enough, round the corner of the barn came an enormous bird which seemed, for a moment, to have Compo gripped in its talons. Then the spectacle resolved itself into Compo wearing a costume in the likeness of an immense pigeon.

'What's been keeping you?' asked Foggy impatiently.

'Listen, big mouth,' urged Compo, joining us, 'this is not the easiest costume to take a leak in.'

'Where's Syd and the van?' asked Foggy rhetorically. 'We want to achieve lift-off before it gets dark.'

Compo asked nervously, 'Am I going to be all right?'

'Of course you are,' Foggy reassured him. 'We've got you a helmet haven't we? Built to British standards and capable of withstanding enormous impacts.'

'What enormous impacts?' asked Compo, clearly unreassured.

'Just a figure of speech. So that you'll realise how safe you will be inside this helmet.'

'But,' protested Compo logically, 'there's only going to be a small bit of me inside the helmet. What about all the other bits?'

'Well, a number of them you might be better off without. The point is you must take every care when you come down to land on your head.'

'Aye but – '

But his new objection was lost in the roar of Syd's van as it swung into the field.

Not much more than an hour later, Compo, poised gracefully on the roof of the van with wings outspread and looking every inch a small scruffy Yorkshireman pretending to be a pigeon, was ready for take-off. At a word from Foggy, Syd put the vehicle into gear and it was soon roaring at speed – nearly ten miles an hour – down the gentle slope while Compo started majestically flapping his great wings in preparation for the glorious moment when Syd would brake sharply and he would soar off into the wild blue yonder. And that, just seconds later, is exactly what happened, except for one small change of plan. Instead of soaring up into the wild blue yonder Compo plunged down into the lush green grass lavishly adorned with cow pats. He now maintains that hang-gliding is the sport of imbeciles and is thinking of taking up grass tobogganing, whatever that may be.

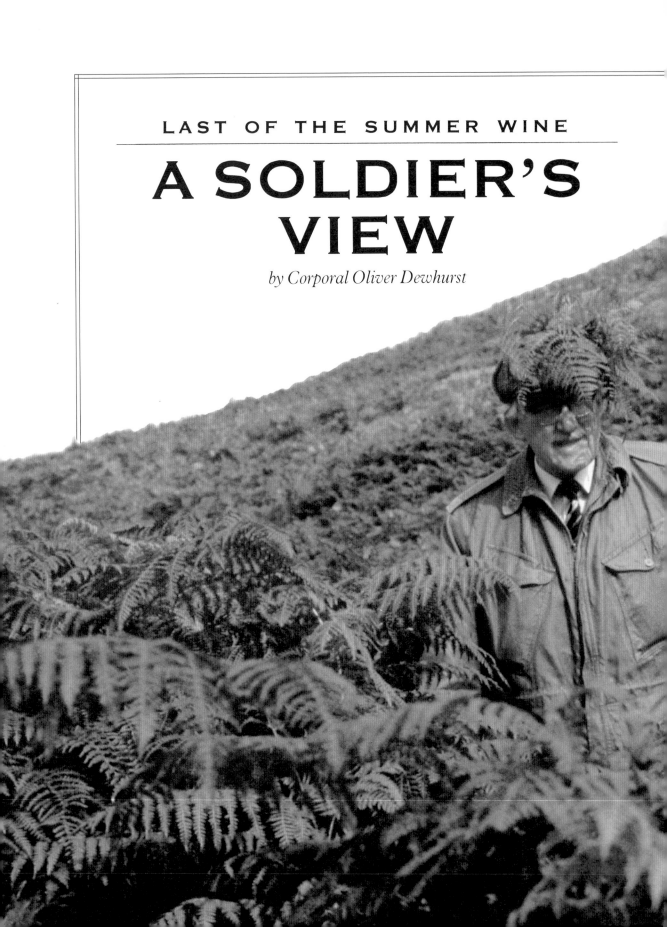

A SOLDIER'S VIEW

by Corporal Oliver Dewhurst

Well now, Cleggy has asked me to write a chapter on the martial arts for his book. What book? Exactly the question that sprang into my mind. I had no idea Clegg was writing a book, but he assures me that he is. No reason why he shouldn't, I suppose, although I've personally always felt that there's rather a glut of the things these days, especially in places like libraries and bookshops. Still, there's no doubt that a genuine demand for them exists or people wouldn't write them, would they? And, of course, I certainly don't want to run books down. Good heavens, no. I was brought up on the classics – Dickens, Thackeray, Agatha Christie and all the other grand old names. And there's not many nights that I don't read for an hour or two before going to sleep. Of course, my tastes have changed somewhat over the years, and if you were to look at my bedside table these days you'd be more likely to see a biography of some famous person like Winston Churchill or Montgomery than even the best novels.

Now, what was I saying? Oh yes, Clegg and his book. I hope it won't sound immodest if I say at the outset that in my opinion he's come to exactly the right person for a section on military science. I mean, I served in a famous line regiment and there's very little about warfare that I don't know. Oh yes, tactics, strategy, logistics, armed and unarmed combat – I've mastered them all. It sometimes makes me shiver to remember the kind of person I have to sleep with every night. A bad dream, an almost reflex motion of my lethal right hand, and I could wake up screaming with a broken leg. I've tried wearing boxing gloves in bed in order to reduce the risk but that makes it virtually impossible to switch out the bedside lamp.

Well now, let's see, the problem is really where to begin. It's such a vast subject. When Clegg asked me if I would write the military chapter for him, I enquired what kind of book he was aiming at. I hoped this would give me some clue as to the kind of contribution he hoped to get from me. But all he said was that he intended it to be a country guide to West Yorkshire. This puzzled me slightly and I asked him if he really felt that a treatise on the martial arts would be appropriate for a book of that kind. Without a moment's hesitation he replied:

'Oh yes, definitely.'

FOGGY DEMONSTRATING THE FEARSOME ONE-HANDED GAROTTE PERFECTED BY HIS REGIMENT.
COMPO AND I ARE LAUGHING BECAUSE, AFTER TRYING FOR NEARLY FIVE MINUTES, FOGGY HAS
STILL NOT MANAGED TO CHOKE HIMSELF TO DEATH.

I must admit that I do sometimes find Clegg's philosophy of life a trifle
enigmatic. Still, I am one of the few local experts on the modern arts of war,
even if there is normally very little scope for practising them in the vicinity of
Stonefirth. I mean, when you are served short measure in a country pub
(which happens far too often in these slipshod times) it would be thought
rather too demonstrative to despatch an armoured brigade equipped with
lavish air support to manifest your displeasure. Then again, should a farmer
shout at you for frightening his lambing ewes while you're legitimately
crossing one of his fields on a well-marked public right of way, it would be
considered excessive retaliation if you blew his farm to bits with accurate
mortar fire. So is it any wonder that someone like me, whose life has been
tuned to the sound of battle, for whom the camp and the field of honour
represent almost exactly the same things that home and office do to most men

– can you wonder if such a fellow feels perpetually a little lost and alone? I tried to explain something of this to Compo and Clegg only the other day.

We were out on manoeuvres. Of course, that's not the way those two would describe it. They usually assume that we are simply, in their endearing phrase, mooching about. They do not realise that I am ever alert for the military significance of the terrain, noting topographical details to be remembered lest we three should ever have to take to these very hills as guerrillas in defence of our homeland. Anyway, as I've said, we were on patrol in the vicinity of Stonefirth and, as usual, the other two, lacking the sheer physical fitness that I have acquired

FOGGY SUPERBLY CAMOUFLAGED AS A FERN.

during my years on the barrack square, were puffing and blowing a bit because we were climbing a little hill, hardly more than a ridge really, but which tested their feeble stamina almost to its limits. I had dropped behind a bit to consult my map since, as the only one amongst us with a scientific knowledge of map-reading, I was, as usual, doing the navigating.

Compo, inevitably I suppose, saw fit to make a feeble joke about my necessary halt.

'Hey up, you're the one what's been driving us on like Volga boatmen. Who said tha could stop for a rest?'

There was a stiff wind blowing and, stung by this absurd taunt, I unwisely looked up from my route-finding to explain the purpose of my pause. Just then, the wind unexpectedly hurled the map into my face with some force. Needless to say, no wind is strong enough on its own to destabilise a trained commando such as me, but unfortunately a sudden thought made me careless for a fraction of a second. I suddenly remembered an incident long ago when a German corps commander tried to finish me with a flame-thrower. His plume of deadly flame would undoubtedly have fried me into something resembling one of Syd's sausages but my lightning reflexes caused me to spin backwards into the Paratrooper's Roll. I was later relieved to find, once I'd taken out the score or so of Germans who had surprised me, that I had, because of my swift reflexes, suffered nothing worse than a single scorched eyebrow. The map slapping me in the face had produced precisely the same reaction and I had flipped backwards without conscious intent. Righting myself a split second later, I found the other two grinning inanely down at me and so I explained the situation to them.

'Did you see how I did that? Catlike on to the ball of my feet, knees bent to absorb the shock? And then over I went, instinctively, into the Paratrooper's Roll. Oh, it's second nature to me.'

Compo, with that ingrained scepticism which is one of the many less pleasing sides to his nature, asked, 'Did tha do a lot a parachuting then as a Corporal Signwriter, Foggy?'

The question evoked in my mind, as it would do in that of any old soldier, an uncontrollable burst of harsh memories. I lived again descents by parachute through a hell of flak, attacks when one had to take out a whole squadron of tanks with only a pocketful of hand grenades, fire-fights on collapsing bridges paved with mines and hung with booby traps – far, far too much to be conveyed to, or even understood by, any civilian. I cleared my throat and said simply.

'Like most of us who were there I – I don't really like talking about it. That's why you two must have noticed me sometimes in a room crowded with people and yet somehow – remote. The jaw set firmly. The lips tightly sealed. Not really stand-offish, but just experiencing the inescapable loneliness of the warrior. All of us veterans remain bowed a little under the weight of our terrible knowledge. We all understand intuitively that we are forever separated from our fellow human beings.'

Compo said something coarse which I won't dignify by repeating but Clegg, who in spite of his often somewhat eccentric views has considerable depths of understanding, nodded and said thoughtfully, 'Yes, it must be a lonely life – the Way of the Samurai.'

'One becomes accustomed,' I murmured quietly. 'Just so long as no one ever asks you to talk about it.'

'Right,' said Compo. 'We won't.'

'Good,' I returned. 'And you too, Clegg? Will you give me your word you won't ever ask me what it was really like?'

'Certainly, Foggy.'

I looked keenly from one to the other, grateful of course, and yet unable to dismiss a slight sense of wonder at their placid lack of interest. Again the terrible scenes flashed through my mind. I sighed.

'I was never one to brag anyway,' I explained. 'You win a chestful of medals. But do you go swaggering about with them? Of course not. You put them away in a drawer somewhere and forget about them.'

'Is it true,' asked Compo, 'that tha never got closer to action than the Naafi at Folkstone?'

I smiled my mirthless smile. Why spoil his peace of mind with the horrible scenes locked away in my memory? Let him preserve his childish innocence.

'Come on, you chaps,' I said sternly, 'or we won't make the Roebuck for lunch.'

The Roebuck, as you probably know, does a pretty good ploughman's and we washed this down with several pints of the rather spectacular best bitter on tap there every Tuesday and Wednesday lunchtime, which is one of the reasons (in addition to my unending military preparations) why we often pass that way on those days. Having passed that way, I was a trifle put out when, not more than half an hour after leaving the establishment, both Clegg and Compo passed out. One minute we were mounting a stony path at a gentle pace and the next they were both stretched out on a grassy bank with hats over their faces. Not liking to continue without them, since they lean heavily on my navigating skills, I sat down to study the terrain while they slept. The next thing I was aware of was Compo's voice.

'I were up this morning at half past three dancing round me bed,' it said. 'Dost ever get cramp, Foggy? Foggy, we've been asleep nearly an hour. It's time to wake up.'

'You two may have been asleep,' I corrected him. 'I have been determining which of these hills would be the easier to fortify and defend.'

'Which of the clouds, tha means. Tha were flat on tha back.'

'Yes, just then I was. Taking sightings of the sun in order to determine the best line of fire.'

'Cramp is agony,' said Compo feelingly.

I smiled eloquently.

'Agony?' I echoed him. 'I'm afraid you simply don't know what agony is.'

'Well, it made me sweat I'll tell thee. Back of me calf all knotted up like Nora Batty's stockinged legs. It's me only complaint about that woman. She has terrible wrinkled stockinged legs.'

Clegg removed his cap from over his face, sat up and said, 'Maybe her stockings are all right. It could be her legs that are wrinkled.'

Compo started to say something, but I interrupted him. I decided that I would make one last attempt to reveal to him that there are sterner things in the world than wrinkled stockings and, if I failed, then as far as I was concerned he could wallow in ignorance for the rest of his days.

'Nobody,' I said solemnly, 'knows what agony is really like till they've had trained knuckles digging into certain fatal pressure points known only to those of us who have undergone the ultimate in combat experience.'

'How would you know about the ultimate in combat experience, Foggy?' asked Clegg, affecting a puzzled manner. 'After all, you've never been married.'

I realised he was trying to lighten the mood and I smiled gratefully. But Compo, naturally, could not resist a sneer.

'That's only because no lass would have him.'

'Really?' I asked, unable to hide a pitying smile. 'Have you ever heard of Jane?'

'If tha means Jane Petrie down at riding stables I've not only heered of her but I've –'

I interrupted hastily: 'I mean the Jane in the famous wartime cartoon strip.'

'Oh, tha means t'lass what were always losing her clothes? Aye, I remember her. What's she got to do wi' it?'

'It just so happens that the cartoonist used me as a model in several of Jane's best adventures.'

'Oh, very likely!' said Compo mockingly. 'Pal of yours, were he?'

'For a time, yes. Before I went overseas. He visited our regiment one day in search of inspiration.'

'And found you?' exclaimed Compo incredulously.

'Precisely. He asked me if he could draw me and then, having done so, he requested my permission to use me in his cartoon strip. As a matter of fact, I was able to help him out with a few plots too. There was, for example, one he used based on an incident that occurred when I was on leave and walking with my father on the cliffs near our farm.'

'And you bumped into a flaming panzer regiment, I suppose?' sneered Compo.

'We saw a Messerschmitt shot down by a Spitfire. The pilot baled out safely but his rubber dinghy became detached and hit me on the head. I used it to row out and rescue him in rather mountainous seas. Of course, in the strip, it's Jane that does the rescuing. I had dinner that night with the charming girl who was the model for Jane and we chuckled about it for

FOGGY, DRESSED LIKE AN AVENGER, SHOWS HOW TO IMMOBILISE A SMALL, SCRUFFY YORKSHIREMAN.

45

hours.'

'Still, it is true that you never married, isn't it, Foggy?' asked Clegg, seriously.

'Yes, it is,' I agreed. 'We soldiers have to make these sacrifices. No little woman waiting at the cottage door. Never the patter of tiny feet. I fear that not being able to browse around Mothercare is one of the major snags of being a professional killer.'

'Thee. A professional killer?' scoffed Compo.

'I don't like to make too much of these things,' I said firmly. 'But if the need ever arose, I could take out a sentry with just one hand.'

Before Compo could provoke me further, Clegg, sensing trouble, tried again to calm matters with a jest.

'I expect if the poor sentry's only got one hand,' he suggested, 'he'd be very grateful for being taken out by anybody.'

I chuckled appreciatively and then got to my feet.

'Onwards, men,' I said firmly. 'I want to check out the ruined chapel as a possible machine-gun post.'

It's sad really. If the balloon ever does go up again, there'll be a great demand for people like me who have military experience and a detailed knowledge of terrain. We'll be needed to play many roles in the defence of England. You can talk of electronics and satellites until you're blue in the face, but did you ever see an electron in deep undergrowth gazing down at an enemy encampment and noting significant details of its defences? When did you last see an electron, perhaps disguised as a simple-minded old peasant (a role tailor-made for Compo), making his apparently aimless way back to his own lines to report on troop movements? How many electrons can live off the land, keeping their bodies fit and their minds alert on just a carrot or turnip and a gulp of fresh water a day? Do you see what I'm getting at? Scouts. The key figures in any guerrilla operation from the time of Alexander the Great to the present. That's what I could train Compo and Clegg to become if I could only get them to see the importance of it – scouts! Oh, I make attempts now and then to institute a training programme but the co-operation I get is at best half-hearted.

A SOLDIER'S VIEW

Just this last Tuesday, we were in rough terrain out near Tucker's Farm when Compo's head suddenly rose up in the middle of a field of ripening oats with a cry of, 'Hey up! Can somebody tell me why we're crawling about here like three duck eggs?'

I rose too from my place and said sternly, 'I can tell you that you're three yards south-south-east of the rusty watering trough and you're dead.'

'I'm dead sick of this lark,' grumbled Compo. 'Why are we doing it anyhow?'

'For Heaven's sake man, you're getting expert, free tuition in how to blend into your background.'

'I don't want to blend into my background. I want a pork pie and a pint of Gallagher's.'

Clegg also rose up out of the oats.

'I wouldn't mind a drink either, Foggy.'

'Good heavens, Clegg,' I said wearily. 'I had expected you to realise the importance of being inconspicuous as regards the background.'

'Oh I do,' he conceded. 'Although in Compo's case I suspect there's an even greater need of him being made inconspicuous as regards his foreground.'

'Look chaps,' I said affably since, like all good commanders, I appreciate the importance of keeping my men happy and hence loyal. 'It's only a little after twelve. We've got plenty of time before lunch to learn how to cross an open space. And then we'll have earned our pint.'

'Now listen, Daphne,' said Compo sarcastically. 'I know all about crossing open spaces. Tha puts one foot in front of the other until tha gets to the other side.'

I chuckled tolerantly.

'And by the time you reach it you'll have enough nickel-steel inside you to sink a barge. I'm talking about how to cross an open space under enemy fire. I'll demonstrate how it's done.'

'Oh dear,' said Clegg. 'Will the demonstration be dangerous?'

'Certainly not. Now you see the road about fifty yards away? What I want you to do is keep your eyes firmly fixed on it. Watch it like hawks.

THE BIGGEST BICYCLE PILE-UP EVER TO OCCUR IN WEST YORKSHIRE.

Because I'm going to cross it right in front of you and I'll wager you won't see a thing. At most you'll think there's a slight ripple in the air.'

'Raspberry or chocolate fudge?' asked Compo facetiously.

I smiled indulgently and ignored him.

I advised them, 'Now I'm going to disappear into cover. I'm going to ground. Don't get panicky if you don't see me for a while. I'll still be there. I could even be within inches of you and you won't suspect a thing.'

And with those words I side-stepped briskly and dropped into the Scout's Crouch. Unhappily, there was a peculiarly prickly thistle immediately behind me and I immediately rose again with a cry.

Compo eyed me in wonder.

'Tha was right, Foggy. It were just like a ripple in the air. I can hardly believe tha got to the road and back in the time.'

'Are you hurt, Foggy?' asked Clegg solicitously.

'I was just testing your reflexes. You should have been prepared for a trick like that and ready to repulse me. You failed that one all right.'

'Which is odd really,' mused Clegg. 'Because Compo's usually good at being repulsive.'

'All right,' I said. 'This time it's for real. Now you see me and – now you don't.'

And I vanished into thin air.

Oh, it was child's play reaching the road. And by the time I'd reached it I had turned into a small bush. Naturally, a small bush would have been easily spotted darting across a road, and so I had to wait for a diversion. Five minutes later one arrived – a bicycle club outing. There must have been twenty or thirty cyclists sweeping down the hill towards me. I waited until they had rounded the bend and then, when I judged that Compo and Clegg would have had their attention diverted, I sprang forwards. Unfortunately, the small bush I had tugged from the ground for camouflage had an unexpectedly long and trailing root and, when I was half-way across, this tripped me up.

There is simply no excuse for the sort of language that several – well fifteen or twenty – of those cyclists used. Quite possibly it really

A SOLDIER'S VIEW

COULD COMPO CONCEIVABLY BE CONSIDERED
A MILITARY ASSET?

was the biggest cycle pile-up ever to occur in West Yorkshire, but you'd imagine members of a cycling club would be skilful enough to swing in an orderly fashion round a small bush in the road. No one was seriously hurt and so I think it is legitimate to take pride in the fact that, until the cyclists began flying through the air in all directions, neither Compo nor Clegg had spotted me.

For all that, it saddens me to admit that forging a corps of scouts from the human material (if Compo can be thus classified) in the Stonefirth area is a challenge that would have daunted General Montgomery. But, looking on the bright side, there are times when my military expertise does prove invaluable. Simple human occasions these may be, but they matter to those caught up in them. Nora Batty, to give the simplest and most human example I can think of, used to be very free with her yard brush when she was displeased with Compo, and many a bruise has he sustained. But since I've taught him the elements of bayonet use, he has become so expert in avoidance techniques that she has stopped trying to clout him with that heavy brush. As a military achievement this does not, I freely admit, rank with the battle of El Alamein, but it gives me quiet satisfaction none the less. And with that I think I'd better say 'Cheerio, chaps'. I have to be up half the night as usual, planning our route for another testing day tomorrow.

WILD FLOWERS

No book which aims at being a country companion can be considered complete without a section on wild flowers. This is a bit odd, really, because you never actually see anyone taking much interest in them. What people around here do take an interest in is discarded consumer durables. I doubt if anyone in Stonefirth would give a second glance at a foxglove as big as a fir tree. But let a rusting, thirty-year-old moped, with both its wheels and also its rear mudguard missing, appear in a field and admiring crowds soon collect. Its beauty and utility are much discussed and sooner or later someone will sneak out to it at night, uproot the little darling and take it home to plant in their own cottage garden.

WILD FLOWERS

But, of course, that's just the locals. The visitors are naturally quite different. Or are they? Nowadays, most visitors snake through the valleys in motor cars. It is, of course, conceivable that as they speed past they (or their passengers) are scanning the ground for wild flowers, but if so it is in vain. The lesser spotted bogwort, like the tooth-petalled marsh celandine, not to mention the purple trailing meadowsweet and indeed virtually every other flowering plant, is a shy creature quite certain to retreat hastily into its burrow when it perceives a car hurtling towards it.

Mark you, I have to confess to considerable feelings of sympathy with those who never learn to recognise even the commoner wild flowers. When I was much younger and contemplating the problem of securing a mate for life, it occurred to me that women, being romantic creatures, would certainly be impressed by a suitor who displayed an easy familiarity with wild flowers. I thereupon invested in a comprehensive guide to the local flora and spent hours poking about in hedgerows and dank coppices seeking plants to identify. But I never became very good at it. It seemed to me that a dismal transformation came over any plant which was unfortunate enough to attract my interest.

There on the page glowed a superb specimen of the – let us say – yellow-striped cabbage lily, with its great petals sharply streaked with neat, pencil-thin saffron lines. Could this really be the same plant as the bedraggled vegetable that I had found cowering under a thorn bush? At the end of several months of assiduous study, I felt on fairly safe ground in identifying the common buttercup but that just about exhausted my repertoire. And when I did finally secure a companion to walk beside me down life's path she turned out to be far more interested in film actors than in anything with leaves and petals.

I once asked Compo what his favourite wild flower was and he replied 'Nora Batty'. Ask a silly question! But the case with Foggy was quite different. When, in another context, I asked him the same question, a kind of greedy leer spread over his face and, rubbing his hands together in a manner unpleasantly suggestive of some of the more avaricious characters in the novels of Charles Dickens, he said firmly 'The Christmas Tree.'

Now the sages of China, and for all I know the onions as well, have always maintained that all things are connected. I am not in a position to verify this profound concept at a planetary level. But I can affirm that the two remarks I have quoted above, seemingly totally separate in both spirit and sense, came together one afternoon in a most striking manner in Syd and Ivy's elegant dining establishment.

To begin with Foggy's Christmas tree, he Compo and

COMPO'S FAVOURITE WILD FLOWER.

WILD FLOWERS

LUNCH IN A COMFORTABLE INN.

I had been out mooching most of the morning and had taken lunch in a comfortable inn. While Foggy was at the bar ordering our refreshments, Compo and I noticed that he appeared to have fallen into conversation with a tall, rough-looking chap wearing a sweaty T-shirt. It is true that, deprived of the confirming power of the nose, it is not easy to establish for certain that a T-shirt on the other side of a crowded room is sweaty, but we both felt that everything about the young man suggested that his T-shirt was unlikely to be as fragrant as the rose. Then Compo asked me if I knew that a camel could run faster than a horse and I observed that it was a pity that they never raced camels at Doncaster or he might have made a fortune and he replied that what I'd said wasn't logical and I pointed out that I'd never claimed it was and soon we were off galloping round the old conversational track once more. And so, we forgot all about both Foggy, at least until he turned up with the beer and slabs of veal and ham pie, and the bloke in the sweaty T-shirt.

After our excellent lunches we resumed mooching, or at least Compo and I assumed that was what we were doing. But it turned out that for once a purposeful power was guiding our steps. No, I am not referring to God but to Foggy Dewhurst. And the fearsome truth only emerged after we had all taken a short nap in a hollow on a hillside in tribute to the excellence and quantity of the Old Yardley's best bitter we had consumed at lunchtime. Then, as I lay for a while after waking up, gazing alternately at the sky and at a small white flower I had absently plucked, I asked Foggy the question I have already specified.

'What's your favourite wild flower, Foggy?'

There was no answer which, since discourtesy could never be considered a Dewhurst vice, surprised me. I turned my head and saw that Foggy was sitting with his knees drawn up gazing out across the valley with a strange smile on his face. I repeated the question and it was then that he turned to me with gold-lust written all over his countenance and said gloatingly, 'The Christmas Tree'.

'The what?' I asked in astonishment.

This innocent query produced another strange reaction from Foggy. He glanced about narrowly as if fearing that industrial espionage agents might be lurking behind every bush before lowering his voice and repeating, 'Christmas trees. Didn't you see him?'

'See who?'

'The forest ranger I was negotiating with in The White Hart.'

At this, Compo who had, up to this point, been giving his celebrated after-lunch imitation of a scruffy log, opened his eyes and asked scornfully:

'What forest ranger? Not the great lump in the sweaty T-shirt?'

'The garment was malodorous,' conceded Foggy. 'That was one of the factors that convinced me that he was genuine.'

'Right, a genuine ponging yob!' said Compo.

Foggy chuckled tolerantly and reached into his breast pocket. He withdrew from it what appeared to be merely a folded sheet of paper and handed it to Compo.

'There you are,' he said. 'I think I have just pulled off the bargain of the year. Ten pounds.'

Compo had by then unfolded the sheet revealing a roughly drawn map.

'Ten pounds?' he echoed incredulously. 'For a bit of an old map?'

'It's not Captain Hawkins' buried treasure?' I asked anxiously. 'You've not bought Captain Hawkins' buried treasure from a stranger in a pub?'

'Hey up!' maintained Compo urgently. 'I'm not doing any digging. Not with my back.'

'No, it's nothing like that,' protested Foggy and then, unwisely, added, 'What kind of fool do you think I am?'

This was clearly too good an invitation to ignore and so Compo and I, speaking in unison, embarked on an exhaustive answer. But Foggy waved us silent, proclaiming hoarsely, 'The Forestry Commission is having a Christmas sale.'

'The Forestry Commission?' I echoed blankly.

'Yes, you've heard of it, haven't you?'

'I've heard of it all right. I've just never heard of it having a Christmas sale.'

'That's where I've been so lucky,' gloated Foggy. 'You've never heard of it because it hasn't been announced yet. But that chap at the bar was the one man in this area who knows about it.'

'And who,' commented Compo pointedly, 'is no doubt half-way to Carlisle by now with your ten quid.'

Foggy said dismissively, 'Rubbish, he was the area forestry officer.'

Compo exploded into raucous laughter.

'That sweaty prawn in the T-shirt?'

WILD FLOWERS

Sensing that this exchange could go on indefinitely, I intervened with, 'But tell us, Foggy, really – what have you actually bought?'

In a smug voice Foggy obliged.

'Christmas trees. A hundred for ten pounds. How's that for a bargain?'

This conversation took place on a hot day in early August, but it was not only this fact that caused Compo and me to gaze at him in stupefaction.

'Down there,' proclaimed Foggy loftily. 'Those are my trees. Let's go and inspect them.'

He pointed across the valley to where, on the lower slopes of the adjoining hill, towered a stand of Forestry Commission evergreens.

'There are a lot more than a hundred trees there, Foggy,' I pointed out. 'And since they're about fifty feet tall, it'll be a bit of a squash getting even one of them into the average living-room.'

'No, no,' he protested. 'My trees will be planted in amongst the big ones. Mine will be small trees that will be just the right size come Christmas. I'm bound to get at least a fiver each for them. Think of it, five hundred pounds for a tenner investment. My goodness I wish I'd bought five times as many. Right, on your feet. We're going to inspect them.'

'We're not, Foggy,' I said firmly. 'Or at least I'm not. It must be five miles to that plantation. But I'll tell you what, when you get to Syd's place about tea-time, I'll buy you a cuppa to celebrate. How's that?'

Foggy turned to Compo and asked wistfully, 'You'll come, won't you?'

Compo sighed deeply.

'I'd like to, Foggy. I always did like inspecting Christmas trees, especially in midsummer. But I've just remembered. I forgot to feed me ferrets this morning.'

And despite Foggy's loud and reproachful protestations, which we could hear, although more and more faintly, for a surprisingly long time, Compo and I made off at speed in the direction of Stonefirth.

That very afternoon, a conversation relevant to Compo's devotion to local married ladies generally held to be of uncertain allure occurred in the home of one of them. I will give you the gist of what was said. But, you object, how can I possibly know since presumably I was not there? True, I was not.

But the husband of one of the ladies did happen to be present (although this fact was not known to the women) and later told me much of what passed between them. Wally Batty was, at the time, communing with his pigeons in his pigeon loft which was immediately above the living-room where his wife was entertaining Ivy to tea and cakes. Since his floor, which was their ceiling, was flimsy he was able to hear every word. Now Wally Batty is not, of course, in the same class as Albert Einstein when it comes to brain power, but he does have quite a good memory for conversations. This one, it seems, began with a brisk canter round the problem of keeping the home tidy. Nora gave it as her opinion that 'Old vests make lovely dusters.'

Ivy agreed enthusiastically.

Nora continued, 'If it won't shine with an old vest it won't shine at all.'

Ivy pointed out, 'Mind you, your Wally's so small, I'm surprised you've got enough vest to do more than one window.'

'Small has its advantages. At least you have no trouble getting into every corner.'

'Which brings me to why I wanted to see you,' said Ivy gravely. 'There's someone else who has no trouble in getting into every corner. Your neighbour – him down there with the clutching hands. Small and obnoxious.'

This could only be, Wally realised, a reference to Compo and he listened even more attentively in the hope of picking up some intelligence that might be of use to his friend.

Nora commented feelingly, 'You don't have to warn me about him. I've been dodging him for years.'

Ivy said bitterly, 'He grabbed me in the kitchen this morning!'

'Came up behind you?' asked Nora with almost professional interest.

'Yes.'

'Quick feint with his left hand and then waps it to you with his right?'

'That's it.'

'Ooh, I know his every move.'

'He nearly made me drop the chip pan.'

'You should have,' exclaimed Nora fiercely. 'Down his trousers! The sooner it gets covered in batter, the safer it's going to be for everyone of us

WILD FLOWERS

To help Compo impress the luscious Nora, Foggy and I agreed to serenade her. But she spurned our efforts, driving Compo — well, batty . . .

round here.'

'But it isn't everyone, is it? It's just you and me. That's why I thought we ought to have a talk.'

And then, as conspirators always do when getting near to the crunch, these two 'wild flowers' lowered their voices. And so, when their steel trap closed, which was shortly after Foggy joined us in Syd and Ivy's café later that afternoon, Compo had to face the peril totally unwarned.

'Hey up, how were the Christmas trees?' asked Compo, taking a large bite out of a jam doughnut and then pursuing with his tongue a considerable quantity of jam that had escaped to trickle down his chin.

'Magnificent,' pronounced Foggy and he did, in fact, seem in buoyant mood. 'I fear you two missed a golden opportunity.'

BLISS BECKONS.

'Really?' I asked, genuinely intrigued. 'How do you mean, Foggy?'

'Well, when I got to the spot where the trees should have been, they weren't there. You were right, Cleggy. The ones on the site I pointed out to you turned out to be massive great things which would have cost a fortune in fairy lights. Quite unsuitable. I was so disheartened that if you two had been with me I might have been tempted to cut you in on the deal for a third each.'

'Such selflessness. Such nobility,' I observed.

'But then do you know what I realised?'

'What did tha realise?' asked Compo thickly, spraying chewed doughnut around.

WILD FLOWERS

'I realised I'd been holding the map upside down. You might be astonished at such an error by someone with my military experience but you see there was no arrow indicating north on the thing. When I had discovered my mistake, I soon re-oriented myself and proceeded to the correct spot.'

'Where the trees were smaller?' I asked.

'Precisely. They were just seedlings, in fact. Barely out of the ground. I have no doubt they'll be in prime condition by Christmas. Or by Christmas next year at the very latest.'

While he had been talking, Foggy had taken out his map and spread it on the table in front of him. It attracted the attention of Syd who was passing with his wiping-cloth.

'What you got there then?' asked Syd.

He picked it up and looked at it closely. He frowned slightly.

'It's one of Gilbert's, isn't it?' he asked.

Foggy and I exchanged a glance.

'Er – Gilbert?' asked Foggy, and I noticed that his voice had suddenly become rather hollow.

'Aye, the bloke that goes round pretending to be a forestry man. Flogs the trees to tourists and any other suckers he can find. He's been done for it twice already and told that next time he's caught he won't get just a suspended sentence.'

'Oh, that Gilbert?' gulped Foggy, looking decidedly unwell. 'Ah, well now – if we're actually talking about precisely the same Gilbert – I mean, should that happen to be the case –'

But it was hopeless and Foggy knew it. Not only had he lost a tenner, but he'd effortlessly achieved the little-coveted title of dunce of the month. Syd gazed down at him expectantly. Foggy almost quivered with the effort to dream up some way of avoiding the terrible admission and then, as in all the best Westerns, at the very last moment the cavalry arrived. Through the door, glamorously dressed, carefully made-up and looking as close to being high-class courtesans as two decent Yorkshire housewives possibly could, swept Ivy and Nora Batty. The two ladies swung round the tables, heading for the kitchen at the back of the café, and, as they passed Compo they both gave

LIKE A RABBIT FLEEING A FERRET.

him a cheeky smile and a little 'follow me' tilt of the head. Compo sat for a moment, gazing after them like one who beholds the gates of paradise swinging open before him. Then he rose looking more like an automaton than a scruffy little lecher and followed them stiffly through the swing doors.

WILD FLOWERS

After that there was, for what seemed quite a long time, silence. In fact, I was beginning to wonder if, against all the odds, Compo might indeed at long last be tasting the delights of amorous dalliance with his two beloveds, when the silence was at last broken. An astounding din, compounded of clashing saucepans, yells of pain and screams of anger erupted in the kitchen. They continued for a full minute and a half until Compo came stumbling back into the dining area. He was pale with terror and minus his fearsome trousers. This had the effect of exposing to view his even more fearsome long-johns, down the front of which a kind of glacier of thick yellow batter was oozing. He shot past our table like a rabbit fleeing a ferret. It was clear that he was motivated exclusively by the need to put as much space as he could between himself and the two harpies who, screaming with triumph and brandishing batter ladles, now came charging after him. Careless of the reception he might get in the open street dressed, or rather undressed, as he was, Compo tugged open the door and vanished from view. Nora and Ivy contented themselves with standing in the doorway and hurling very unladylike jeers and gestures after him. I turned to Foggy.

'Well there you are, we all have our burdens to bear. And on the whole I think your Christmas trees are a doddle compared to Compo's wild flowers.'

Foggy heaved a deep sigh. His countenance remained stony.

'Not much use keeping this, I suppose,' he said wearily.

He began tearing the deceitful map into small fragments . . .

'There,' he said, when he'd finished. 'It's just confetti now.'

'Then you'd better keep it in case either Ivy or Nora relents and Compo gets one of them to the altar.'

Foggy looked at me like someone whose tragic destiny put him beyond the reach of mere frivolity. After a moment of two he said thoughtfully, 'You know, I could have been wrong about him. That is, about his degree of physical fitness. Some day I'd like to time him over the hundred metres. There just could be an Olympic-class sprinter there.'

I smiled. After a moment Foggy, if only faintly and ironically, smiled back. But after that, of course, it wasn't long before we were both laughing helplessly.

WATER SPORTS

by Compo (and Clegg)

Well now, Cleggie has aksed me to rite this chapter on water sports and its funny really what the fust thing I thinked of were. Well, it were Chunky Wigglesworth, weren't it? And duz tha want ter no why? Corse tha duz but before I git that far, I better tell thee why it is that Clegg thort I'd be rite for this 'ere chapter. Its because I do more water sports than both t'uthers put together. I mean, how often does tha see Foggy on water skis or come to that Cleggie down in depths wi' a snorckel on? Just about niver is the answer.

So then wots all this about Chunky Wigglesworth? Is he sum kind of sooperman at water sports or wot? Well he wos right enuff but not in the way tha's thinking. I'll have to tell thee wot us three were on about in Syd's t'other day. Foggy and Clegg seemed to think it were my turn to pay for teas and I were ferreting about – 'ere that's a good 'un wen tha thinks I often do 'ave a ferret down there – but this time I didn't and –

So wot do you think has happened just as I were riting? Clegg only came in and looked over me shoulder. Then he sed I wasn't riting it good enuff and so he would have to rite it itself. Which is orlrite by me.

∗∗∗

Oh dear. I do hope you don't mind the above line of asterisks, but I did feel the need for a good strong barrier to keep Compo's prose from getting out. I'm letting his opening remarks stand only because I feel it's important that readers should understand why I felt I had to put a stop to them. The reason is certainly not because I want to hog any glory that may flow from writing this little book. On the contrary, I'm eager to get all the help I can. Foggy has already contributed an excellent chapter on martial arts, and any more chapters I can acquire without having to do the writing myself would be more than welcome. For all that, what editor with an ounce of compassion in his nature could lay before his audience a whole chapter written in Compo's style? It would haunt his conscience to the end of his days.

I should concede at once that what Compo says in his last paragraph is absolutely true. I did look over his shoulder and express – well, rather strong reservations about what I saw. It happened like this.

About a month ago I asked Compo if he would write the chapter on water sports for this book and he sportingly said he'd have a go. Then, a few days ago, I called round at his place (on my own since Foggy was at the dentist) to see if the little fellow felt like a spot of two-handed mooching. I knocked several times on the door of his somewhat subterranean quarters but received no answer. I knew the door would probably not be locked since

Compo, even in his absence, usually permits access to his home to any creature not less well behaved than a wild boar. Compo himself, I felt, must have stepped down to the corner shop for a tin of ferret food or a puncture repair kit for his wellies, and would not mind if I waited for him within. I pushed open the door and entered.

Imagine my surprise at seeing Compo himself seated at his rustic kitchen table, so engrossed in sucking on a stub of pencil that he had apparently been unaware of my knocking. Spread out before him was a large but grease-stained sheet

THE 'AUTHOR' IN HIS STUDY.

of paper that looked as if it might originally have been wrapped round a portion of fish and chips. On it, as I could see from the door, was some writing. What could Compo be at work on? A love letter to Nora Batty? An application to Oxford University for the chair of English Literature? The one thing I did not think of was what, in fact, the document proved to be – his attempt to write the chapter on water sports that I had asked for weeks ago.

I stole up behind him and peered over his shoulder. And what I read, with growing dismay, was what I have printed above on the other side of that stout wall of asterisks.

'Compo, are you working on what I think you're working on?' I asked cautiously.

He was in a state of such intense creative concentration that he showed not the least dismay at my popping up behind him like the demon king in a pantomime.

'Aye, it's the chapter on water sports,' he conceded at once. 'How dost think it's a'comin?'

'With all the grace of a waltzing elephant,' I said, perhaps a trifle unkindly.

'I thought tha'd appreciate it, Cleggy. I think I've got a real knack for this writing lark.'

'But there is one teeny little problem.'

Compo set down his pencil stub and leaned back in his seat. He looked distracted like one abruptly summoned down from the heights of Parnassus to the mean perspectives of everyday life.

'What would that be?'

'I think the publishers intended the book to be in English.'

'Well, what dost think it's written in?'

'I was hoping you might tell me.'

'It's the English I've always spoke.'

'And therein may lie a little problem.'

I tried to put my reservations as gently and tactfully as I could, and in fact Compo soon began to see that there was some justice to them. Within little more than an hour he had admitted that, although endowed with

WATER SPORTS

MESSING ABOUT IN BOATS.

astounding literary talent, he still found writing a dull pastime, and would sooner any day be engaged in groping Ivy while she screamed with revulsion or else in communing with his ferrets. It was agreed amicably that I would take over the chapter from him, as I am now doing. And since I am doing it, I suppose I must also grasp the nettle that Compo has planted for me and continue with his item about the odious Chunky Wigglesworth. Well, what Compo was clearly intending to say about Chunky can be put quite simply. Compo was about to tell readers that Chunky was, in fact, the school champion at – no perhaps in a family publication of this kind it can't be put quite so simply. Anyway, the essence of the matter is that Chunky had this phenomenal ability to – well – all right, you know what a wall is and you know how competitive schoolboys can be and – oh, let's get it over – Chunky could pee higher than anyone else in our school. So there you have it: Compo's notion of an outstanding athletic achievement.

And now to more savoury aspects of the sporting life. But – water sports? I think I can imagine the objection that will be going through the minds of many of my readers. What have the Yorkshire Dales to do with water sports? Am I confusing the grassy hills of our fair county with the blue billows of the Caribbean or the fun-packed beaches of the Mediterranean? Not at all. I have always proclaimed that the person who experiences all that Yorkshire has to offer will feel no need for any other place on Earth, and especially not Wales. And in this chapter I intend to prove that proposition.

It started one moderately good mooching day last year when we found ourselves on the river bank. We stood and gazed at the broad, placid stream and Compo, possibly yielding to the tranquil spirit of the place, asked a daft question: 'What makes water wet? I mean why does it feel different to dry?'

Foggy replied sourly.

'I have no idea, but I'm very grateful that you have at last started to take an interest in the subject.'

Then Compo asked an even dafter question. This is one of the little man's truly impressive talents. You think after he's asked a daft question that no human creature anywhere on the surface of the planet could ask a dafter one and then, often within seconds, he asks it himself.

'Why is there a big, dark man with a window in his head swimming around down there?' was the triumphantly daft question he asked on this occasion.

Foggy remarked to me that Compo was the only person he'd ever encountered who could have a nightmare while he was wide awake, and I was about to ask whether Compo could ever properly be said to be wide awake when a big, dark man with a window in his head rose up out of the river and growled at us.

'Why don't you bog off you lot?'

Compo drew back in alarm, crying, 'Hey up, I think it might bite.'

Dismayed by this turn of events, since how would Foggy and I be able to sustain our sense of superiority if Compo started asking sensible questions, I queried anxiously, 'What on earth is it?'

Compo replied, 'I don't know, but it looks terrible fierce.'

The strange aquatic being gave tongue again.

'You think you've found a quiet bit of water. Miles from anywhere. And it's like the bleeding bus station on market day.'

Foggy exclaimed, 'I know that voice. Not to mention that bad temper.'

And Compo completed the identification.

'It's Syd from the caff.'

And Syd from the caff it did indeed prove to be. There could be no mistake since, as it waded ashore, the creature from the black lagoon pulled

ALL THE NICE GIRLS LOVE A SNORKELLER.

back what proved to be a snorkelling mask and revealed the all-too-familiar face of Syd from the caff.

'I'm in trouble now,' growled Captain Nemo as he clambered up on to the bank. 'I'm right in it now. You try to pursue some little hobby quietly and the river bank is suddenly lined with spectators.'

'Dun't Ivy know tha dresses up in this sort a gear then, Syd?' asked Compo sympathetically.

'No, she doesn't,' admitted the other. 'And I'd like to keep it that way.'

'Good God,' exclaimed Foggy. 'A bit of snorkling's not a criminal offence.'

NO, NORA HAS NOT BEEN CROWNED QUEEN OF RUSSIA. SHE IS MERELY GOING TO THE ANNUAL TEA DANCE OF THE PIGEON BREEDERS' ASSOCIATION. COMPO IS BIDDING HER A FOND FAREWELL.

'It somehow sounds like one though, doesn't it?' I suggested. 'I mean, what a terrible thing to find on any man's record: unlawful snorkling in a public place.'

'Wives never understand,' grumbled Syd, divesting himself of his rubber skin. 'They don't understand the masculine urge to test yourself to the limits in some alien environment.'

'That reminds me,' I said thoughtfully. 'I have to call at the post office on the way home.'

Compo asked, 'Does tha really enjoy messing about in rubber suits, Syd?'

Syd replied morosely, 'I'm going off it rapidly. It's not worth all the trouble. I'd sell the whole damned outfit for a fiver.'

Sensing interest, Syd held out his hand palm upwards towards Compo who, to our amazement, promptly slapped it with his own palm and exclaimed 'Done!'.

WATER SPORTS

But then, of course, Compo found that he just happened to have no money on him. This was something that just happened to him all the time but Foggy, to my amazement, actually volunteered to lend him the fiver.

'Why?' I asked Foggy, eyeing him closely to see if he was showing any other symptom of mental disorder.

Foggy shook his head irritably.

'I just feel,' he said, 'that I can't back out now. Not after spending years trying to encourage him to become more familiar with water.' He sighed and looked down at the five pound note he was getting ready to hand over to Syd. 'Mind you, I hate parting with these things. I've never been much of a one for dogs or cats around the house, but nice clean little five pound notes really bring a lump to your throat.'

Thus it came about that two or three weeks later I stood on the river bank, quite near to the spot where Syd had emerged from it, gazing uneasily at the water's unbroken surface while Foggy sat comfortably in the shade beneath a tree wittering on about the charms of the season.

'I must say,' he murmured. 'I like this time of year. The long evenings are very pleasant.'

I scanned the river's surface intently and began 'Er – Foggy –'

He apparently failed to hear me.

'There's nothing quite like the English twilight,' he opined. 'It's not the same out East you know. Darkness comes down all of a sudden out there.'

'The thing is – Foggy –' I tried again.

'Wallop! And that's it. Your tropical night drops like a dustbin lid. No, I'm very fond of this time of year in England.'

'I don't want to worry anybody, Foggy – but –'

'It's about this time of year I get this well-nigh irresistible urge to go out and buy a pair of sturdy boots.'

'Tell me something, Foggy.'

'It's amazing what satisfaction there is to be had in the selection and purchase of a good pair of sturdy boots.'

'How long is he supposed to stay under water?'

'What?' asked Foggy, gazing in my direction at last. I pointed to the water's surface.

'Oh,' he said, finally realising what I was getting at. 'I believe it's optional, isn't it?'

'Don't you think it's about time he was coming up?'

'Oh, I don't see why. Maybe he's met someone congenial down there. Many of these rivers are stiff with snorklers these days.'

I peered again at the surface.

'I can't see any bubbles,' I urged.

But Foggy remained unperturbed.

'Well, he's only a beginner – probably hasn't got the hang of bubbling properly yet.'

'Well, I think we ought to do something.'

'Excellent idea. Why don't we compare boots? It'll take our minds off

him which is always a plus.'

'No, I meant do something for him.'

'Oh, for him? Well, I suppose we could. It's just that it feels instinctively wrong to start plucking him out of the water when it's taken all these years to get him in.'

'Well, what should we do? Shout?'

'That only works if you have your mouth under the surface. Otherwise he won't hear a thing.'

'Really?'

'Oh yes. I mean when did you ever see fish popping to the surface to investigate a loud noise?'

So, with some difficulty and discomfort, which involved lying flat on the bank and consuming several pints of brackish water, we ultimately managed to get our mouths under the surface and shout, or rather gurgle, 'Compo! Compo, are you all right?'

'Quite all right, thanks,' came his answering voice, so clearly he might have been on the bank immediately behind us.

'Where are you?' I gurgled at the top of my gurgle.

'On the bank just behind thee.'

'I see, and when – what?'

Foggy and I both sprang to our feet and turned. And sure enough there was the little scruff, water dripping from him, looking like the creature from the black lagoon's even more horrible kid brother.

'How did you get here?' Foggy asked suspiciously.

A BOAT MIGHT HAVE BEEN MORE EXCITING BUT COMPO JUST COULDN'T AFFORD ONE.

WATER SPORTS

'On me own two flippers. I come up in them reeds down yonder.'

But I found myself quite overwrought and scolded him like an anxious mum.

'Well, how dare you come up safely out of sight when we're trying to save your life right here?'

Foggy shook his head disdainfully and said, 'I don't know why we bother.'

Compo, pulling off his mask, echoed this.

'And I don't know why I bother either. Dead boring this skin diving. Can see more in a darkened cinema before the film starts. I've had enough of it.'

'Really?' asked Foggy, sounding distinctly disappointed. 'Then what do you want to do?'

'Water skiing,' said the little daredevil.

And quite soon that's just what he was doing. Well, it would take altogether too long to describe how Wally Batty made him a special pair of custom-built, satin-smooth water skis which had only one flaw – the boots on them were too big for Compo's feet. As a result, whenever Wally started his forward run with the motor cycle he was using to tow Compo, the little man shot out of his boots into the river. On one occasion, when Wally suddenly found a Forestry Commission Land Rover approaching him on the narrow towpath, and was going too fast to stop in time, he swung off on to a side trail. As a result, Compo remains to this day our local record-holder in water skiing through a forest. He is proud of this achievement and maintains that it was well worth the two days he was laid up in the cottage hospital.

But perhaps the best water sport of all in the Stonefirth area remains falling into a river or pond. Compo undoubtedly holds the world and Olympic titles in this testing athletic activity, and glories in his long run of success. The only thing missing, in his opinion, to make Stonefirth a resort comparable to Cannes or Palm Beach is the admiring presence of Nora Batty in a bikini. He asked her once if she would oblige in this way, but she simply hit him with her yard broom without replying . . . It was in the days before Foggy had taught him how to parry properly, and he sustained a nasty contusion.

WILD ANIMALS

The first and most important thing to be said about wild animals is that, for all intents and purposes, they don't exist. By that I mean that you never see them, hear them, smell them, touch them or perceive the least sign of their existence. But what is odd is that the people who write books about the countryside do not seem to have grasped this simple fact. In order to make clear what I mean, I am compelled to make a shameful admission. I once took a holiday outside Yorkshire. No, don't jump to the conclusion that I was so depraved as to visit Wales. I am happy to report that I have never sunk that low. But in my early married years, when I still sought the elusive key to making my beloved happy, I agreed one year to her wish that we should holiday somewhere other than in Yorkshire. Her suggestion was that we might spend a fortnight in London, but I had read about the pitfalls that lurked in the great city for simple country folk like us and I managed to dissuade her from any such perilous expedition. In the end we settled for the Lowlands of Scotland, which I hoped – rightly as it turned out – would be similar in atmosphere to my beloved West Yorkshire. But what was different, of course, was the local geography. Not knowing our way around as we did in Stonefirth, and yet wanting to explore the local countryside, we were reduced to purchasing a walks book. When we first examined the contents of this volume a certain apprehension sprang up in both our minds. For the book gave the impression that the surrounding landscape teemed with wildlife to an extent that made the Serengeti plain of Africa seem a lifeless waste. Would we be safe? Should we arm ourselves with large-bore rifles before venturing off across the menacing heather?

The next day after breakfast, book in hand, we set off to attempt the first walk recommended by the author. We soon reached the bridge over a stream where, we were informed, the walk was supposed to start. Here, our guide informed us, we would undoubtedly see a stoat dart out of the undergrowth, cross the path ahead of us and lope off across the meadow on the other side of it. Aware that the stoat, while not actually a man-eater, is a formidable scrapper with needle-sharp teeth, we kept a sharp eye out for its arrival. It became clear, however, before very long that this must be the stoat's day off. Hawks, our book affirmed, would quite certainly be circling overhead, scanning the ground below to locate a juicy morsel for breakfast. However, uneasy glances skywards reassuringly failed to reveal the presence of these dangerous predators. And so it went on throughout the day. According to the account guiding our footsteps, birds and beasts in immense variety should have been running, stalking, circling, leaping, darting and cavorting all about us. In fact, apart from a friendly mongrel that approached us from a cottage garden with lolling tongue and wagging tail, and the usual assortment of miscellaneous small birds in the middle distance, we saw no sign of the brute creation from start to finish. The Scottish Lowlands, we concluded, were really much like West Yorkshire as regards the reluctance of its wildlife, assuming it to be there at all, to step forth and be counted. The only difference was that the local authors seemed to have rather more febrile imaginations.

In actual fact there really are fearsome monsters at large in West Yorkshire, but you have to know where to look for them. I recall a whole afternoon searching cautiously through dense undergrowth in the hope of locating some to photograph. It was in the old days when Cyril Blamire rather than Foggy was the third member of our little band of musketeers. It is now many years since Cyril, against our fervent advice, went off to live in some outlandish place like Guatemala or Wales and Foggy came out of the army to join us. Anyway, the point is that Cyril was a photography fiend and we often had to help him in his unending attempt to win photography competitions. He never succeeded, but he did amass a good collection of fascinating snaps. On the occasion in question, Cyril had managed to persuade Compo and me, against our better judgement, to help him flush out some fearsome creatures so that he could get a shot at them before they managed to inflict any damage on us.

I can still recall the thrill of excitement we all felt when, after a long search, Compo, with an audible intake of breath, exclaimed, 'There's one!'

'What's it like?' asked Cyril.

'Massive, with thick brown fur, big horns and tremendous staring eyes. Real Hammer Horror it is.'

Cyril, very, very cautiously, joined Compo at his post.

'Where is it?' he asked softly.

'There on that leaf.'

'It's a caterpillar,' sighed Cyril, clearly deeply disappointed. 'I thought I'd made it clear – I'm looking for beetles.'

But as regards the really big stuff, the truth is that the only wild animal, other than rabbits which hardly count, that we meet with any regularity does not live in the wild at all. It lives in Compo's pocket. Come to think of it, how wild can an animal get? I'm quite certain that if I were a wild animal and was offered the choice of living in the most nightmarish, fever-ridden swamp or in Compo's pocket I wouldn't hesitate an instant before choosing the former. Actually, the real mystery is not so much that the ferret seems to enjoy his place of residence as that Compo seems to like having him as a pocket guest. I mean ferrets, like the stoats I mentioned earlier, are predators and have razor-sharp teeth. You might think that a ferret in a pocket would, from time to time, come over all peckish because it has missed its mid-morning snack and have a good poke around in search of meat. It seems, therefore, little short of miraculous that Compo's tenor singing voice, although of a quality

A WILD, UNTAMED CREATURE — WITH A FERRET PEEPING OUT OF HIS JACKET.

WILD ANIMALS

that causes our choir master to blanch whenever he is accidentally subjected to it, has not suddenly changed into an alto.

I have never really understood why Compo keeps ferrets at all. He claims it is in order to supplement his meagre food supply, and certainly chasing rabbits from their holes into a net is the traditional role of the nimble little creatures amongst the rural poor. But I have never yet seen Compo either eating or cooking a rabbit and I strongly suspect that, like everyone else, he lives on a diet of fish and chips, beefburgers and the occasional jam doughnut washed down with tea at Syd and Ivy's elegant café. I think the ferrets are just for swank, although no doubt he has by now developed an affection for them. Certainly, whenever he goes on a trip he takes them with him, a habit which has, on occasion, produced quite astounding quantities of chaos in boarding-houses.

The fact is that animals as a class, other than Compo's ferrets, do not play a very large part in our lives. The hills around here are alive not with the sound of music but with the sight of sheep, and of course we invariably have to wade through a flock or two of these when out mooching. We sometimes also meet and exchange friendly greetings with the odd cow or horse. In other words, our encounters with the dumb creation have almost always been affable. The only animal that I can recall giving us a really hard time was neither a wild one nor a domesticated one but a member of that group euphemistically known as household pets.

It all began one glorious day in late June, when, after a jolly morning mooch, we laid ourselves down in the shade of a small grove of trees on a bed of soft, fresh grass and quite close to a stream whose pleasant gurgle accompanied our conversation. I kicked off with a riddle.

'What has six legs, is slimy and has a face under its feet?'

Compo, who was lying on his back with his hat, which is not quite so vile as his trousers but bad enough in all conscience, over his face, instantly said, 'I give up.'

Foggy rebuked him.

'You're supposed to think about it a bit. Not just give up.'

'Sorry,' said Compo contritely. 'OK, I've thought about it. Now can I give up?'

Foggy, who was seated with his arms clasped round his knees, now raised his arms to heaven as if in supplication.

'Isn't it marvellous,' he exclaimed, 'when you consider that Old Mystery Trousers here is of the same species as Albert Einstein.'

At this Compo removed the hat from his face, sat up and, with a puzzled frown, said, 'I don't remember any Albert Einstein. Was he in our class?'

LIFE'S A RIDDLE.

'God preserve us,' implored Foggy. 'He probably thinks William Shakespeare was one of the lower-form masters.'

'I do not,' jeered Compo. 'I know quite well he were manager of the canteen down at girls' army camp. Some of them were grand lassies. I remember one called Janey or Joaney who, if tha gave her a glass or two of whisky, would always let tha – '

'Be still,' ordered Foggy imperiously. 'You are a conversational disaster area. You could debase and trivialise a discussion between philosophers.'

'Between Phil Ossifers and who else?' asked Compo cheerfully.

'I will not exchange another word with you,' said Foggy sternly. He turned to me. 'What was that riddle again, Clegg?'

'What has six legs, is slimy and has a face under its feet?'

A frown of concentration appeared on Foggy's face and remained there for a minute or so. Then he sighed and shook his head.

'No, that's a tough one. What's the answer?'

'I don't know,' I replied. 'But you've got one crawling on your cap.'

Naturally Foggy leaped to his feet, tore off his cap and beat it fiercely against a tree to dislodge the non-existent intruder (since it had been a practical joke and not a riddle at all) and it was then that the white poodle hove into sight.

'Hey up!' said Compo, pointing. 'Somebody's made a right boggle of shearing that sheep.'

Foggy ceased punishing his cap, inspected its top closely and then replaced the garment on his head. He joined Compo and me in staring at the gorgeously trimmed and manicured, snow-white French poodle that had just come sniffing into our little grove. The animal paused when it saw us, granted us a long, superior look and urinated against a convenient tree. It then trotted haughtily out of sight into some bushes by the stream. Hardly had it vanished than a red-faced chap, wearing an anxious expression, followed it into our midst.

'Have any of you seen a dog?' asked the chap, catching sight of us.

'What make?' asked Compo.

'Well it answers to the name of Fifi, so naturally it's an Irish wolfhound,' returned the other with, I felt, unnecessary sarcasm. I forgave him, however, because I perceived the sweat on his brow and realised that he must have been having a very trying time. He mopped some of the moisture away with a handkerchief as he seated himself near us.

Foggy pointed in the direction that the gorgeous animal had taken and said helpfully, 'It went that way.'

The man started and asked fearfully, 'What, towards the water? Is it deep?'

'What's the difference?' asked Compo unfeelingly. 'It can swim, can't it?'

'How do I know?' asked the man, showing signs of resignation. 'All I ever see it do is eat flaming toffees, lick the wife and pee all over me geraniums.'

'Still,' pointed out Compo reprovingly, 'it's thee that takes it for a walk.'

'Not by choice,' said the man firmly. 'I get ordered out by the wife.'

Foggy asked reasonably, 'If it's her dog, why doesn't she take it?'

The man laughed a short, bitter laugh.

'She's fatter than the dog is. She spends all her time chomping toffees too. Oh well, I'll have to go find Fifi, I suppose. No help for it.'

And with obvious reluctance he got to his feet and stumbled away in the direction the animal had taken.

'It's always a pleasure,' I remarked, 'to see someone happy at his work.'

Foggy frowned and suggested, 'He should have kept it on the lead.'

Compo shuddered and pointed out the obvious truth.

'Would tha like to be seen fastened to a thing like that?'

But a moment later Compo and I were both electrified by a new note sounding in Foggy's voice. Where it had been – only seconds before – tentative and low, it now suddenly rang out with a blood-curdling decisiveness that we had both experienced before. Getting to his feet, the Montgomery of Stonefirth uttered the following war-cry.

'Yes, yes, I tell you. If it

were organised on a proper commercial basis. If we were being paid for it. There must be hundreds like that fellow who would seize the opportunity to have their pets exercised properly by some competent third party. Where are you two going?'

We were, of course, going as fast as our feet would carry us towards any place where Foggy was not. We had both instantly recognised his seizure as the latest in his long list of catastrophic money-making schemes.

But he caught us before we could get very far. He usually did, having longer legs and probably slightly better wind than either Compo or me. And he began to paint the usual picture of limitless affluence ahead which somehow always managed in the end to persuade us to join him in his crackpot ventures. He had, it seemed, just experienced a vision and it had told him that the future lay in dog-walking. Today Stonefirth, tomorrow England and an office in every town and village. But this would be the mere preface to the mighty drama.

'Then one day,' Foggy intoned in a voice like a great amen, 'the phone's going to ring. And it's going to be them.'

'Them?' asked Compo looking distinctly alarmed. 'Which them?'

Foggy stopped dead in his tracks and stood rigidly to attention, as he had done so many times during the superb full-dress parade of his crack regiment: 'The Fifth Signpainter Commandos' or was it the sixth? He said reverently:

'The royal corgies.'

'Tha don't mean the little buggers can use a phone?' asked Compo in awe.

But Foggy was now locked into his dream and there was no stopping him.

'It will mean the royal warrant on our letterheads,' he began. 'It will mean we'll be in with a chance for the OBE. Perhaps ultimately I'll be Sir Ralph Dewhurst OBE. Of course, privately, amongst the household, I shall still be known simply and affectionately as Foggy. Sandringham will then mean early morning mist and Foggy out with the corgies.'

Foggy broke off, apparently gazing with inner eye at the glorious future he envisaged in the grounds of Sandringham. Then he abruptly pointed towards a nearby house and said briskly, 'That's where we'll start.'

'Tha daft prawn,' sneered Compo, 'that's not Sandringham.'

'Of course it's not,' agreed Foggy reasonably. He had apparently recovered from his seizure and was his old, tolerably rational self again. 'But it's a substantial dwelling. It's clearly inhabited by the kind of people who can afford to have their dog taken for a walk.'

'Maybe they haven't got a dog,' Compo suggested logically.

'Of course they have,' scoffed Foggy. 'Prosperous rural citizens always have dogs.'

We had meanwhile been approaching the large, double-fronted house set in fine grounds. Now Foggy pointed triumphantly at a small, white plaque on its gate.

'What did I tell you?' he enquired smugly.

'Not that tha wanted to get thy backside chewed off!' protested Compo. 'Does tha not see? It says "Beware of the Dog".'

Foggy laughed in a superior way. 'No dog is dangerous if you know how to handle it. I did a dog handlers' course in the army. Part of the basic training in any elite commando unit. You'll see, I'll have it jumping through hoops in no time.'

With which he flung open the gate and advanced down the long, crazy-paved path towards the front door. Compo prudently pulled the gate shut after him and we both leaned on it to observe Foggy's progress.

He did not, in fact, get very far. He had advanced little more than ten yards along the path when there came a deep baying sound from the back of the house. It had a peculiarly sinister note. Foggy stopped dead in his tracks. Just so must Sir William Baskerville have halted when, out for a pleasant stroll, he first heard echoing across Dartmoor the howl of the fearsome hell-hound that was the ancestral curse of his family. Foggy glanced back at us. We smiled encouragement. He took another, and rather less resolute, step forwards. Round the side of the house bounded a small grizzly bear. Or so it appeared. It was really a monstrously overgrown specimen of that species of dog which wears its hair over its eyes but somehow manages to find its way about without benefit of a white stick. Baying like the Baskerville curse, it lolloped towards Foggy at astonishing speed. Foggy wasted no time attempting to handle the creature but turned and bolted back towards us. We pushed open the gate for him to dash through and then slammed it shut to prevent the advancing fury from following him. Then the three of us drew back a few paces and contemplated the overgrown brute, which was now standing on its hind legs, resting its front paws on the gate and bellowing with rage and the desire to rend and tear.

'That is a very fortunate dog,' gasped Foggy. 'There are techniques for subduing badly trained animals such as that one. Rather painful techniques. I nearly succumbed to the impulse to use one. But, of course, it would be unethical to train the animal without the consent of the owner.'

'Well, why don't you knock at the front door and request it, Foggy?' I suggested. 'I'm sure the owner would be glad of your help in educating Rover.'

'That's not why we're here,' objected Foggy. 'We're in the process of founding a dog-walking service. It would be a poor advertisement for it if we took that unruly beast on the public highway. Come along, we'll try the next house.'

Compo and I needed little persuading and so we all strode away from the snarling brute. We had gone perhaps fifty yards when I became aware of a curious phenomenon. The snarling from behind did not seem to have become much quieter. I glanced over my shoulder. The monster had, apparently, leaped the gate and was lolloping after us. We were mounting a fairly steep hill and it struck me as unlikely that we would be able to outrun the animal. I looked about for some refuge but all I beheld was a very old Land Rover mounting the steep road at a crawl.

'Why don't we get in the back of that Land Rover?' I suggested. 'Be a lot easier than walking.'

I pointed at the vehicle.

'We can't do that,' protested Foggy. 'Not without asking permission.'

'Pity,' I said sadly. 'It might also save us being devoured.'

The other two, alerted, glanced backwards and, seeing immense jaws yawning just behind them, joined me in a twenty-yard dash which resulted in the three of us scrambling into the back of the Land Rover just ahead of poochy. At about the same time, the vehicle reached the top of the hill and, the driver apparently quite unaware that he had unexpected guests in the rear, began to draw away from the pursuing beast. It seemed we were saved.

'Hey up,' exclaimed Compo, 'it's not giving up.'

He was right. The dog, although now outpaced by the Land Rover, was still bounding after us.

'Ridiculous animal,' said Foggy haughtily. 'I almost regret now that I didn't give it a short, sharp lesson in manners.'

'You may,' I said, 'still get that chance.'

The Land Rover had abruptly come to a halt and we all three suddenly remembered that at the top of the hill we had been climbing was a T-junction with its 'GIVE WAY' sign. The dog, which had not been far behind, now approached at what seemed astonishing speed. With a clunk of gears the Land Rover began to get moving again. But it was too late for us. With a leap which, in such a bulky creature, was as astonishing as it was graceful, the great shaggy animal rose into the air and came down in front of Foggy. The near-impact unbalanced Foggy and he fell over backwards. And then it was demonstrated that we had all been quite wrong about that dog. Its breast was not filled with savagery and hatred at all. Quite the contrary. Its behaviour had apparently been dictated by a bad case of love at first sight. For it now seated itself comfortably on Foggy's chest and, lowering its head affectionately over our friend's, began to lick Foggy's face in long, slow, voluptuous licks.

Needless to say, Compo and I were not slow in seizing the opportunity.

HOME TO STONEFIRTH.

The Land Rover was still travelling quite slowly. We were over the tail-gate and on to the road again in a matter of seconds. Then, as the vehicle pulled away ahead of us, Compo called after it.

'When tha's finished training the dog, tha can sign it up for walkies. We'll see thee in Syd's place about tea-time if tha can tear thaself away.'

Compo and I did an about-turn and began to mooch quite happily back in the direction of Stonefirth.

Enter our GIANT COMPO Competition

WHAT'S IN COMPO'S MATCHBOX?

FIRST BATCH OF ENTRIES TO OUR GIANT COMPO COMPETITION

4. Please, this is a family newspaper! Mike Timberlane, a 'poet and milkman', suggests that, to put it delicately, a **human derrière** would wring a gasp of horror from the modest maidens of Stonefirth.

1. Mrs Susan Sharp of Harper's Bridge thinks that a **MOUSE** might make the girls squeak.

2. **FALSE TEETH** are what Si and Wilf Pangbourne, two 'friends, brothers and pensioners' of Tinkertown Road, believe might upset the damsels.

3. Young Sara Wilberforce, whose mum is a district nurse, thinks a **BIG SPIDER** would be the most horrible thing you could imagine in a matchbox.

5. A **SKULL** is what Tim Brown, a fifth-former at Delbay Primary School, feels sure would frighten 'any girl I ever saw'.

THERE WILL BE A 1ST PRIZE AND A 2ND PRIZE.

1st Prize is a breakfast alone with Compo. **2nd Prize** is a whole day alone with Compo. Draw us what you think is in Compo's matchbox. Our readers will then vote, using the voting slip on this page, for which they think is the best, giving reasons for their choice.

6. Big, pursed **KISSING LIPS** would, according to Miss Marjorie Cudder, who is a secretary, give quite a shock to the average girl. Having trouble with the boss, perhaps, Marjie?

7. Tammy Gilbert, who is five, considers **MR PUNCH** to be the pits.

8. The family Morrison, that's Mum, Dad, Caspar, Corin and Wilhelmina, are firmly convinced that only **COUNT DRACULA** himself would have such a devastating effect on all who glimpse him.

9. And perhaps the most ingenious suggestion of all. Little Patty Summerson, who is a philosopher at the tender age of twelve, insists that Compo's matchbox must open to reveal a **MIRROR**. The most frightening thing in the world, she maintains, is oneself.

LETTER

The Editor,
The Stonefirth Gazette

Sir,
I have been a reader of your newspaper for nearly forty-five years but now I feel I have no choice but to ask you to cancel my subscription. The fourth entry in your Giant Compo Competition last week, representing what can only have been a naked human backside, is an insult to your readers. Is it not enough that we must each of us endure the humiliation of bearing about our person one of these abominable objects without having it paraded before our eyes in the pages of what I have hitherto always considered to be a family newspaper of elevated moral tone?

Utterly Pissed Off of Stonefirth

DON'T BE ALARMED IF YOU MEET AN ASS ON THE PATH.

THE PERILS
OF THE
COUNTRYSIDE

I can only hope readers will forgive me for devoting the concluding chapter of this book to sterner matters than have preoccupied us thus far. But I feel that we would be failing in our duty if we did not point out some of the hazards of the rural life, as well as offering suggestions for avoiding or alleviating them. Now your average yuppy, in his stretched limousine, cruising round Yorkshire sees only a smiling landscape blessed with every delight the human heart could require. I therefore implore him to remember the words of Sherlock Holmes to his colleague Dr Watson when the famous team was working on a case in a rural part of England: 'I assure you, Watson, more peril resides in these seemingly tranquil acres than in the teeming streets of London.' I don't actually happen to have Conan Doyle's magnificent book before me as I write, but the passage was certainly somewhat along those lines.

I cannot do better, in the way of revealing some of this peril, than to recall a melancholy occasion in a country inn four or five years ago. Foggy, Compo and I had called in for a little refreshment and had just seated ourselves with our foaming pints when Compo, gazing with furrowed brow across the room, remarked:

'Hey up, that's got to be Ludovic. No one else looks quite such a complete twit as him.'

We followed the direction of his glance, and saw a pathetic figure slumped inebriated in a seat with his hands covering his eyes.

'Good heavens, the man's in terrible shape,' exclaimed Foggy with that instant sympathy which is perhaps his most endearing characteristic. 'I must see what I can do.'

We all three rose and made our way discreetly across the room to where our wretched acquaintance sat lapped in misery. Having reached him, Foggy began at once.

'We're here to help you, Ludovic, and to assure you that you're not alone. I want to offer you the wisdom and experience of the combat soldier. Former Corporal Dewhurst is at your service.'

The human wreck he was addressing removed his hands from his eyes, glanced up at us revealing dreadful, red-rimmed orbs, and growled, 'Bog off, Foggy.'

Whereupon we three returned to our seats.

I attempted to comfort Foggy.

'Don't feel rejected, Foggy. We'll stick by you.'

I turned to Compo. 'Won't we stick by him?'

'Of course,' growled the uncouth one. 'It's his round next.'

'Ludovic has no sense of style,' observed Foggy. 'But one can't help wondering what's afflicting him.'

'I can make an informed guess,' I offered. 'Raymond Holcroft looked just like that the night before he did something desperate.'

'How desperate?' asked Compo.

'He bought a boarding-house in Mablethorpe.'

Foggy blanched but contented himself, in the tight-lipped way of the warrior, with murmuring aloud, 'Poor devil.'

And without another word, now that we had all three grasped how urgent the situation might really be, we rose again and went back to where Ludovic sat slumped. Compo spoke first.

'If it's a boarding-house, Ludovic, don't do it.'

'Just leave me alone,' groaned the desperate figure in the chair.

I tried myself to reason with him.

'It may look like an easy way out, Ludovic. Many men have made that tragic error. But just remember your relatives.'

An ash-grey countenance was raised to mine.

NO ONE LOOKS SUCH A TWIT AS LUDOVIC.

'What about me relatives?'

'They'll be round every summer expecting free holidays.'

Foggy now added his urgent plea.

'Think of it, Ludovic. Your relatives dropping in, and not just for an overnight stay. For a whole week.'

Compo now proved that, against all expectations, there was good stuff in him. He leaned over the pathetic creature.

'Promise me, Ludovic, before tha buys a boarding-house, just ring the Samaritans.'

At this Ludovic rose to his feet and glared round at us.

'What do I want wi' a flaming boarding-house?' he bawled. 'I've got enough problems without one.'

'You mean,' I stammered, 'it's not a boarding-house?'

And thus it proved. The memory of poor Raymond Holcroft had led me astray. But if you think my error suggests that the cautionary note of this chapter is mere scaremongering, wait until you learn of the nightmare that really was burdening Ludovic. From his broken and halting words we now discovered that, in a moment of total moral collapse, he had purchased not a boarding-house but a motor caravan. And this vehicle, it seemed, was in such a broken down and derelict condition that he could not bear to drive it for fear of provoking mirth and derision in all those who saw him at the wheel. This is, in fact, a classic peril of the Yorkshire Dales which, along with sheep and magnificent scenery, offers a greater number of ruinous old bangers for sale than any other part of England. It is virtually impossible to live for more than a year in Stonefirth, for example, without, in a weak moment, buying some ghastly vehicle that one must then pilot through the public streets. Realising that Ludovic's plight was probably beyond human alleviation, we stole silently away.

Yes, I know what you are thinking. This is hardly a problem likely to affect the yuppy in the stretched limousine. Well, true though that pronouncement undoubtedly is, there are two qualifications that need to be made. One: this book is not aimed exclusively at such exalted beings, but chiefly at the average, decent visitors to our beautiful district, many of whom

GHASTLY VEHICLES.

do, in fact, succumb to the temptation provided by the cheap motor vehicles they find on offer everywhere. And two: yuppies are not necessarily immune to this lure. I once heard of a director of one of the big five, or high street, banks who arrived in Stonefirth at the wheel of a brand-new Mercedes, and left the town a fortnight later carrying his tearful and distraught family in the bowels of an ancient Rolls-Royce which he had rescued from doing ignominious duty as a pigpen on a local farm. The last report we had of him was that, his family having by then deserted him, he was still daily to be seen pulling up outside his palatial offices in the City of London at the helm of this galloping pigsty.

In any case, I have given these examples of the peculiar perils to be found in our district not because they are the chief ones, but because they indicate very clearly the insidious nature of the challenges the unwary visitor may face. Naturally, almost everyone who spends any time in our region arrives well equipped with books indicating which fungi are edible and which snuff you out like a noggin of arsenic. The danger inherent in waving a red rag while crossing a field where a bull is incarcerated is also widely understood. But how many visitors would even dream of the deadly peril in which they might find themselves, as we did some years ago, from practising what the uninitiated would doubtless regard as the harmless hobby of bird watching?

It was when Cyril Blamire was with us, in the old days before Foggy had been invalided out of the Fifth Signwriter Commandos or whatever his

101

regiment was called. Now Cyril was a very keen photographer and he had decided to make a photographic record of all the local bird life. Alas, he never got very far. The first day out, Compo and I helped him to make up a 'hide' in a patch of bushes. We all huddled inside it and Cyril set up his camera, with a telescopic lens aimed at a nest he had spotted on the low branch of a nearby tree. He had only just finished adjusting his shutter speed and twiddling with his aperture – as all serious photographers must do to achieve credibility – when from the long grass beneath the tree rose up Howard and Marina, who had been conducting one of the longest-running clandestine affairs in the history of Stonefirth. These two believed their illicit passion was totally unsuspected, while bets were in fact exchanged as to how much longer it would last. Anyway, as they brushed themselves down, Marina suddenly gave a little shriek of dismay. She had seen Cyril apparently in the act of photographing their most private moments. She pointed. Howard turned and then, snorting like a bull confronted by an insolent red rag, he bent down, picked up a stout fallen branch and came charging after us. He chased us all the way up to the Kidderpore Road, and Cyril's camera was quite badly damaged. That put paid to the great photographic record of local bird life. paid to the great photographic record of local bird life.

No, the fact is that you never know what emergency country life is going to produce. It was for this reason, as well as because he's a daft, romantic idiot, that Foggy started his Citizens' Rescue and First Aid Service. It happened some time ago and I'm not sure now if that was exactly what he called it, but it was certainly something along those lines.

It began on a morning when we had been walking along the canal bank and had come upon a little pile of clothing. Without hesitating even a single moment, Foggy ordered Compo and me to jump into the water in order to rescue the putative suicide. I know that 'putative' is the right word for what I am trying to express, but it is not one I ever enjoy using. Perhaps this is because it sounds a bit like putrid. I certainly don't wish to give the impression that this particular suicide wasn't a perfectly nice and wholesome fellow. As a matter of fact, I can state quite definitely that, whatever his other qualities, he had an excellent sense of humour. While Compo and I were

HOWARD AND MARINA.

splashing miserably around in the freezing stream, searching for him beneath the surface, he paddled up in a canoe wearing canoeing shorts and began to dress from the little abandoned pile of his own clothing. When he finally learned from a red-faced Foggy that the two bedraggled imbeciles in the river were searching for him, he nearly busted some vital portion of himself laughing.

But Foggy was not in the least dismayed. You have possibly read the famous classic novel *Don Quixote* by Cervantes, or at least heard of it? In that case you will probably recall that so fervent was the Don's determination to be a gallant knight that, when he could find no real giants to kill, he charged instead at some windmills, having succeeded in convincing himself that they were the malignant Titans. Well, all I have to say is that Foggy could have given Don Quixote lessons in advanced barminess. Indeed, when compared to our Foggy, the Spaniard emerges as a level-headed chap with his feet firmly planted on the ground.

That afternoon, Foggy arrived at the café to meet us wearing a kind of lightweight anorak with a big red cross painted on both front and back. He was also carrying a small haversack. Compo and I looked at each other and then at the door of the café. But before we could begin stealthily backing out, Foggy glanced up and saw us.

'Good. You're nice and early. We'll have plenty of time for a patrol before tea.'

'What patrol?' asked Compo warily.

'You know that canoeist?' Foggy chuntered on. 'I gave him a piece of my mind. It should be a criminal offence, wasting the time of the rescue authorities.'

'But Foggy,' I pointed out reasonably, 'we're not the rescue authorities. We were just three idiots getting wet on a purely private basis – well, two idiots and their commanding officer.'

Foggy ignored the gibe.

'I grant you we're not exactly the rescue authorities,' he admitted. 'But we are, in fact, something even more precious. We are private individuals with the right stuff in our veins.'

'And in our haversacks? What have you got in there, Foggy?' I asked, indicating his little rucksack.

Foggy opened the container and, as he intoned the list of its contents, he took the specified items out of it.

'First aid kit. First aid manual. Flask of hot, sweet tea, aspirins, torch – battery operated – assorted splints and emergency surgical instruments.'

'Ugh!' exclaimed Compo. 'What surgical instruments?'

'Well, at present they're a Swiss Army penknife and a bent spoon.'

'Oh, a splendid selection,' I said with what I hoped would seem cutting sarcasm. 'I mean there's practically no emergency known to man that you can't alleviate with a Swiss Army penknife and a bent spoon.'

'What I want to know,' asked Ivy, approaching our table to see what

CLEGG'S FIRST GLIMPSE OF FOGGY TOGGED UP AS A RESCUE MAN.

105

OUT FOR A LOVELY DAY'S CANOEING. PITY ABOUT THE WATER SHORTAGE.

villainy was taking place, 'is where did you get the spoon?'

Foggy shook his head tolerantly and explained.

'It's my old army spoon, madam.'

'It had better be,' said Ivy severely. 'Ours are all counted.'

Syd joined us, chuckling at Foggy's appearance.

'Not that we begrudge the odd spoon. In the service of humanity.'

Foggy smiled in a manner suggestive of infinite tolerance.

'They laughed at Florence Nightingale,' he said simply.

Compo grumbled, 'I should think they did, if all she had was a bent spoon.'

Ivy asked Foggy wonderingly, 'And just where do you think you're going, dressed like that?'

'Wherever there is need, madam.'

'You'll get locked up,' she predicted firmly.

'I shall become a figure of hope to all in pain,' Foggy contradicted her, clearly in the grip of his old humanitarian yearning from which any sensible human would run a mile.

Half an hour later we were back on the towpath, only this time Compo was dancing about proclaiming: 'I am not going in the water. I am not going to get soaked through twice in one day.'

'Of course you're not,' urged Foggy soothingly. 'There's no call for it. All we're going to do today is make a few preparations, so that when some poor soul does fall in there'll be something on hand to fish him out with.'

He abruptly stopped walking, raised his hand to shade his eyes and gazed about keenly.

'It's scandalous,' he pronounced. 'Look about you. Not an appliance in sight. There's absolutely nothing here we could use to rescue someone with.'

'Then let's leave it and go for a pint,' suggested Compo sensibly.

Foggy shook his head sadly.

'I really thought this morning's experience might have fired your enthusiasm,' he observed.

'Oh, it did,' I assured him. 'We've both got very fired enthusiasms.'

'I mean,' Foggy expostulated, 'we're now in the rescue business. It's the noblest of professions. Saving decent little people. Didn't it excite you in the water this morning? Didn't you feel anything?'

'I flaming did,' Compo conceded. 'I felt summat wriggling in me wellies.'

'Well, I'll tell you what I felt,' Foggy went on. 'I felt useful. There we were for once – doing something important – helpful – and it came to me in a flash that this is what we ought to be doing with our lives. All right, on your feet. You'll feel different once we've really rescued somebody.'

I tried a last humble plea.

'If it's all the same to you, Foggy, I had planned to just fritter my life away harmlessly.'

'Not good enough,' he came back sternly.

A LADDER IS INDISPENSABLE FOR SAVING A DROWNING PERSON.

'I just thought I'd mention it,' I said sadly.

We marched on for half a mile or so and then, in the vicinity of a ruined barn, Foggy stopped abruptly.

'That's it!' he exclaimed excitedly. 'That's what we want.'

Compo and I gazed in the direction of his pointing finger. We beheld a fairly weatherbeaten ladder propped against the side of the barn.

'It's nobbut an old ladder,' jeered Compo.

'Precisely,' agreed Foggy, sounding in no whit dampened. 'And we have no alternative but to improvise. We simply don't have the resources available to the authorities. It will be ideal for our purposes.'

'A point that occurs to me,'

I ventured hesitantly, 'is that it's not exactly our ladder.'

'Nobody is claiming that it is our ladder. I merely propose moving it so it becomes the general public's ladder. Or that portion of the general public that keeps falling into the canal. Come on, let's get it.'

But we had no sooner set larcenous hands on the ladder than we were startled by a loud thump. We could tell it originated at a nearby crossroads, but could not see just what had happened because of an intervening clump of trees.

THE PERILS OF THE COUNTRYSIDE

'Leave the ladder!' ordered Foggy, his features transfigured and his eyes shining with the true rescuer's ecstasy. 'No time for it now. That was a road accident. Well, come on, men.'

'Yes, but – ' I objected. 'There could be blood. I'm not going if there's going to be a lot of blood.'

Foggy, having unshipped his bag, was already sprinting in the direction from which the bang had come. Now he paused and looked back to me.

'Blood?' he echoed. 'I hadn't really thought in terms of buckets of

blood. I was hoping more for a nice clean break or two. Perhaps a spot of concussion or a touch of shock. That kind of thing.'

'What's wrong wi' blood?' scoffed Compo. 'Personally I like a bit fried in black pudding. All right, if tha won't go cause tha's afeered, I'll do it meself.'

But at this Foggy, seeing his knightly armour in danger of being tarnished, snapped back into his role of leader.

'Of course I'm not afraid. I was thinking of your sensibilities, that's all. Right, now I want you both to stay here until I call. I can't have you fainting and making more work for the ambulance crews when they finally get here. I'll now proceed to the fatal scene on my own.'

And, with a resolute pat on his bag, he hurried on again. Naturally, Compo and I followed him at a discreet distance and, once we had cleared the trees, we perceived what had occurred. There had been an accident all right but one that had resulted in injury to metal rather than flesh. Two cars, noses touching and clearly, even at this distance, severely dented, were motionless in the road while their drivers were anything but motionless. Both were young men and clearly on the edge of physically expressing their displeasure with each other. Compo and I realised at once what was bound to happen, and were so certain of the impossibility of averting it that we simply halted and watched in frozen fascination.

Into the scene of strife and denunciation bounded Foggy and, having satisfied himself that no injured passengers were in need of attention either inside or outside the cars, he immediately adopted the role of peacemaker. We watched as he interposed himself between the two furious young bucks, as he held them apart, as he pushed down their menacing fists with his own firm but pacific hand and, finally, as he received a solid whack on the nose from one of the two antagonists, maddened by his tactless intrusion, and a relatively harmless kick on the shin from the other. A minute or two later, hand over his face, blood trickling between his fingers, and limping slightly, a morose Foggy returned to us.

Was that the end of the Citizens' Rescue and First Aid Service? Even to consider that possibility is to do an injustice to Foggy Dewhurst. He may be a barmpot of a calibre that is rarely seen in the West Riding of Yorkshire, but he is, for all that, one of the most decent chaps I have come across in my earthly pilgrimage. He continued with his self-imposed mission for weeks, with, I fear, decreasing participation from Compo and myself, and sporting a faintly comic bandage over his nose. But, apart from a desperate lamb that had become separated from its mother by a fence and which he was able to restore to the maternal udder, poor Foggy found not a living thing to rescue. I often think it is some kind of comment on the contrary nature of this strange universe in which, without even having applied for a visitor's permit, we all arrive that the only sufferer Foggy encountered in his career as a rescue man was himself.

Have a good holiday now.

Clegg

WALKS
SUPPLEMENT

Introduction by Clegg

Foggy, Compo and I are, of course, born-again moochers. We never know when we advance towards a crossroads which way we will turn when we reach it. Indeed, we are never sure if we will turn in any direction at all. We may instead simply sit down on some convenient grassy spot and have a nap or an aimless conversation or indulge in some merry, madcap entertainment such as playing rugby with Compo as the ball. For us, the delights of the countryside are to be found as much in the absence of necessities as in the presence of possibilities. It is different for visitors. They

naturally want to know where they can enjoy a scenic walk or two without alienating the local sheep or trampling on Farmer Giles' prize asparagus. So how can we aimless moochers help them to achieve these legitimate aspirations? Well, I have given the matter some thought and I have come up with the following plan. Each of us three will write out a description of an excellent walk that we would love to take if we were the kind of people that loved to take excellent walks. And don't panic at the prospect of being subjected to some more of Compo's nightmare prose. I have insisted, with his reluctant consent, that I will edit his contribution into such an inoffensive state that even a timid maiden lady would be able to peruse it without distress. Happy walking.

Clegg's Walk

This walk begins at Syd and Ivy's delightful rustic tea rooms where you and your wife may decide to fortify yourselves with a scrumptious jam doughnut, made as only Stonefirth folk, who obtain them from the gigantic corporation in Manchester that bakes them, can provide. It is delicious washed down with a cup of Syd's expert brew of a liquid not unlike tea. Indeed, I have known visitors to the Dales insist that their brief stopover at Syd and Ivy's was the high point of their whole holiday. This was not just because of the excellent microwave home cooking, but because of the true Yorkshire atmosphere provided by the sound of earnest family conferences issuing from the kitchen, punctuated by the musical note of a saucepan descending rhythmically on to Syd's head.

Suitably nourished, leave Syd and Ivy's – with some haste if crockery should happen to be flying – and take a sharp right up a flight of steps. The way now takes you past an adulterous couple who often sneak a kiss and a cuddle at this relatively deserted spot. Your wife will here sniff audibly and make some comment about rustic morals.

Reaching the top of the steps, you find you have a choice. You can either turn right into the garden of a man called Willie Clutterbuck, continue straight on or take a sharp left. If you take the right, Willie Clutterbuck is very likely to come out and shout abuse at you or, worse still, young Tammy Clutterbuck may take a pot-shot at you with a catapult that he wields with uncanny accuracy. If you take the sharp left, you may easily plummet from a parapet on to a bed of gravel about twelve feet below. For these reasons, it is best to take the path directly ahead especially since, by doing so, you will soon be rewarded by a spectacular view of the municipal sand-pit for under fives.

On reaching the top of the hill, you will see, immediately across the road, a footpath crossing a field on your left. Ignore it. It leads to Charley Vincent's barn where Charley is occupied most days in building the hottest hot-rod in Yorkshire, and if anyone is foolish enough to pass his barn door, which is what the footpath does, he or she is virtually certain to be deafened by an abrupt roar from within and choked by a dense cloud of black smoke shooting out through a broken pane of glass.

Take instead the path that goes round the field to the right. A little care is needed in that Charley Vincent may, on that particular day, have decided to test ride his recently modified trial motorbike instead of working on the hot-rod, and could suddenly shoot out of a side-path spattering you both with mud and inducing your wife to observe that if you had any virile instincts at all you'd chase after him and punish him.

But now you are free of the town confines and all before you is beauty and wild nature. Look carefully to your left as you follow the way-marked trail in a north-easterly direction, and you will see a stoat gallop out of a small copse and cross the path a little way ahead of you. If you don't see it, this simply means that the stoat is staying at home on that particular

day. Look up at the sky and you may see a golden eagle or two circling voraciously. Or again, you may not. What you are virtually certain to behold is a lot of sheep steadily munching grass. It is a scene redolent of the Yorkshire countryside, and guaranteed to inspire in the most determined walker an impulse to have a nap. Do not hesitate. Lie down, put your hat over your face and try to ignore your wife's tendency to grumble non-stop about your lethargic state.

You will wake up much refreshed and wondering if you have had enough of the great outdoors for one day. Your wife, when you have mentioned this speculation, will mock you mercilessly, pointing out that you have undertaken to perform a seven-mile circular walk and cannot, as yet, have completed more than about a mile of it. You summon all your energies and set out once more.

Before long, the way takes you past a ruined chapel on the right. This is well worth a visit, if only because your legs are by now beginning to ache and you will get a chance to sit fairly comfortably on a low wall for a few minutes. While doing so, note the intricate finials on the chapel. If there don't happen to be any finials, don't worry because your wife won't know the word anyway.

Leaving the chapel, follow the hairpin path down into the valley. At the bottom a rushing stream provides a cheerful sound but, as you get closer, a small scruffy man being thrown into it provides a rather less cheerful sound. The small scruffy man's name is Compo, and he is being given his annual bath, much against his will, by his devoted friends Clegg and Foggy. It is recommended that your wife avert her eyes as you pass this quaint rural scene since Compo is quite likely to be clad only in his dreadful underwear.

Follow the brook upstream for about a mile and a half, by which time you will find yourself gasping for breath. But don't despair. As you will see from the map, you now turn left along the edge of an evergreen plantation, and begin to climb much more steeply up the hillside. The reason you shouldn't despair is that the slope soon becomes so incredibly steep that you can plausibly maintain to your wife that attempting to climb it will infallibly induce a heart attack. The only sane course, you can urge rhetorically, is to turn about and retrace your steps back to Stonefirth. Unhappily, your wife will be totally unpersuaded by this argument and, with unkind gibes, will heartlessly goad you on to the very top of the ridge.

While staggering the last hundred yards or so – and on the very verge of cardiac arrest – you will marvel at how fit your wife is when she drinks as much as you do, and eats hardly any more fibre.

But now your reward is at hand. For the next three to four miles you will follow the gently dipping and rising crest of the ridge, revelling in the glorious views that stretch away in every direction. Your pleasure will be marred only by your wife's insistence on discussing her friend Doris's recent hysterectomy, and her apparent indifference to the scenery. Towards the latter part of the ridge walk she will vary the obstetrical observations with the claim that she is quite faint with hunger, and reproach you bitterly with having failed to bring a picnic or even a sandwich along. Peckish yourself, you quiet her with the promise of a slap-up meal back in Stonefirth.

The return journey proves much less challenging than the outward one. A path leads off the ridgeway and, in a smooth and easily negotiable descent through attractive heathland, soon brings you back into town. Your delight in the walk, now that you have accomplished it, is marred only by glancing casually at your watch and discovering that it is after seven o'clock on a Sunday evening. This means that the only place where you can get a meal, since you have neglected, to your wife's almost infinite disgust, to book a table anywhere, is at Syd and Ivy's bear garden and fast-food café.

Foggy's Walk

Right then, head up, back erect and, when you're ready, step out. That's it, nice, loose, swinging stride that devours the miles. Yes, but, I imagine you're wondering, where are we going? Come to that, you might also be asking yourself where have we come from? In other words, where does the walk start and finish? And the answer I have to give you is: it doesn't matter in the slightest. What's that? Am I joking? Not in the least. The point is, how can you tell in advance which way the enemy will come? No way at all. And so we must take into

account all possibilities. Tactically, any given route is as valuable as any other since the enemy's plans, we must assume, are unknown. What? You'd like to know which enemy I'm talking about? Clearly there is simply no way of establishing that at this historical moment. We have no option but to wait and see. You may ask: why must we base our contingency planning for a simple country walk on the hypothesis of preparing for an encounter with a purely notional enemy? And my answer is that I am constitutionally incapable of pointlessly devising a

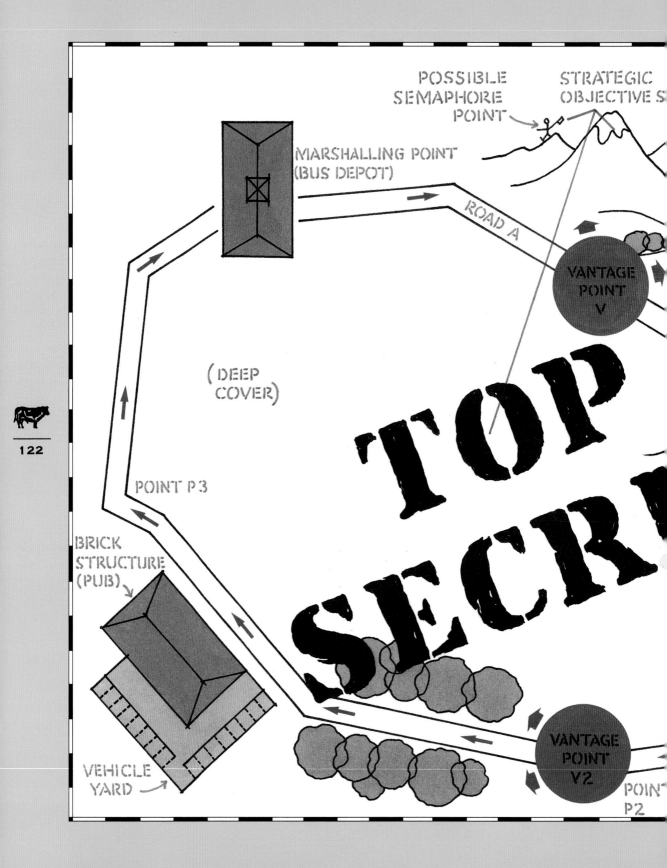

POSSIBLE
SEMAPHORE
POINT

STRATEGIC
OBJECTIVE S

MARSHALLING POINT
(BUS DEPOT)

ROAD A

VANTAGE
POINT
V

(DEEP
COVER)

TOP
SECRE

POINT P3

BRICK
STRUCTURE
(PUB)

VEHICLE
YARD

VANTAGE
POINT
V2

POIN
P2

strategically valueless, civilian, recreational walk. Although it might surprise two fellows I know, and whom I shall refer to – if at all – as Scout X and Scout Y, to hear this, the truth is that when I walk my purpose is almost invariably military. You will see from the map I've provided to accompany this tactical patrol that my knowledge of the region, while exhaustive, is purely strategic in its implications although decidedly tactical in its detail. And it is, of course, the detail, as I seek endlessly to impress

upon Scouts X and Y, that will prove crucial in the event of hostilities.

Right then. Departure from what will henceforth be referred to as the Marshalling Point will be at 1000 hours or, if you have had a late breakfast, at 1100 hours. It is quite in order for me to reveal that the Marshalling Point is the bus depot in Stonefirth since this fact can be readily deduced from the map. Nothing else of tactical significance can be thus deduced and so, for all other data, only code references will be given. This is to neutralise any strategic value the map might have for an enemy should it fall into their hands. To recapitulate, you leave the Marshalling Point by Road A and proceed according to a secret compass bearing for approximately eighteen hundred (1800) yards. This will take you to Vantage Point V shown on the map. From here any mere civilian will doubtless only perceive a superb panoramic view of the Western Dales with the Pennines in the distance.

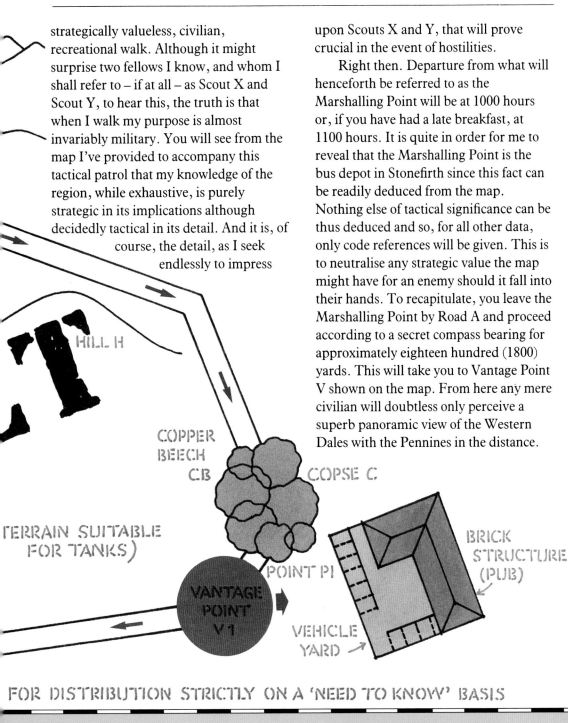

HILL H

COPPER BEECH CB

COPSE C

(TERRAIN SUITABLE FOR TANKS)

POINT P1

BRICK STRUCTURE (PUB)

VANTAGE POINT V1

VEHICLE YARD

FOR DISTRIBUTION STRICTLY ON A 'NEED TO KNOW' BASIS

But the trained tactical eye will discern an excellent location for a strongpoint commanding the southern approaches to Strategic Objective S and capable, if supplied with heavy artillery, of blocking the advance of armour. It is also a good place for a picnic, although you will probably think it is still a bit too early for lunch.

Leave Vantage Point V on a new secret bearing and, hugging the flank of Hill H, swing round in an orderly formation until you reach Copse C. Enter Copse C at Copper Beech CB and traverse the copse, emerging at Point P1. Looking down over the valley from Point P1 you will descry, to the left, a brick structure with a vehicle yard. This is a pub that serves some of the best draught bitter in West Yorkshire. On reaching this point, Scout Y often suggests that we drop down to the brick structure and have a pint or two, an option which is, of course, open to anyone reading this. My own view, which I invariably put forcibly to Scout Y, is that

it is still too early in the morning for boozing, just as it was too early for lunch at Vantage Point V, but that we could buy some bottled beer or cider and some sandwiches for when we reach Point P2 or Point P3. Scout Y is an argumentative little scruff and sometimes gets his way, but I advise you to press on since there is another pub a few miles further on which does just as good beer and food. It is possible, of course, that you have brought your own picnic lunch or had a packed one prepared for you at your hotel back at the Marshalling Point. In any case, you will probably be patrolling with someone a lot more presentable than Scout Y, so you won't be so reluctant to be seen in a saloon bar with him.

From this location, which we will call Vantage V1, a straight and level path runs for almost exactly two miles to Vantage V2. You may decide that this feature of the route provides an admirable opportunity to test both your degree of physical fitness and your speed of march. You may well already wear an electronic stop-watch on your wrist and, if not, I advise you to invest in one and bring it along. You will then be in a position to undertake the test march, bearing in mind that it is unwise to set too rapid a pace initially for fear of not being able to maintain it the whole way. Unhappily, I have myself never yet succeeded in persuading Scout Y to participate in this test march, although Scout X is a perfectly reasonable and responsible citizen, who

If you have, in fact, done the test march, you will probably want to lie down for a few minutes and recuperate. My patrol usually stretches out even though we have not done the march. This is because Scout Y is so extraordinarily idle. Moreover, when he wakes up he tends to howl and plead for lunch and we almost invariably end up by dropping down into the valley, where a part-pebble-dashed brick structure with a vehicle yard is located and can just be seen from V2 down a logger's avenue in the trees. This is the other pub I mentioned and, on balance, I think they do an even better bitter than the first one, although you may find their cheese rolls are stale. I did last week and I complained forcibly about it.

After lunch there is usually a good deal of resting and dozing which has precious little military significance, then you have to make your way back to the Marshalling Point as best you can. There is a bus service or, if you're exceptionally lucky, you may find someone with a car in the vehicle yard who is prepared to give you a lift. I warn you, it's one thing walking out to this vantage point, but it's a lot more testing to go back the same way with a skinful inside you.

Right. Well now, it only remains for me to wish you happy patrolling, and to urge you to convey any sound military intelligence you may have acquired on the march to the War Office in London. Dismissed.

takes my insistence on military preparedness with appropriate seriousness and always joins me in trying to get the little scruff into motion. Sometimes we even roll him ahead of us for a few yards just to emphasise our determination, but he has no military sense and very little patriotism. He just lies there on the trail, looking like an old scarecrow some farmer has abandoned because it got too disgusting with age and now tends to attract crows rather than frighten them away.

When you reach Vantage Point V2, either on a test march or just sort of mooching along, you will perceive that it is an excellent position on which to set up both a machine-gun emplacement and a multiple facility communications hub. Should you have the appropriate equipment with you, I suggest you at least make a start on these valuable additions to the region's military infrastructure.

Compo's Walk

One of my favourite walks is tha goes out on the Leewell Road and keeps going until tha gets to where the road does a right fork and there's a field gate on the left. Sometimes tha might want to stop here and have a bit of a chinwag or sit on the gate and say comical things and suchlike about friends or acquaintances. We never stay much more than twenty minutes or half an hour. So then tha goes up this road, which is just a lane really, until tha comes to a signpost saying 'Footpath' where tha can turn left on to a footpath that takes thee up into the downs. So after about a mile or so, there's a bank on the left with a lot of holes in it. These are rabbit holes and tha would be right in thinking that makes it a good place for poachers but naturally I'm not calling anyone a poacher. What's more

tha's not likely to see one unless tha comes about two in the morning of a moonlit night. What the poachers do, is put nets over a lot of the holes and then turn any ferrets they might have with them down another hole and the ferrets drive the rabbits out into the nets. But tha needs to know where to get thy ferrets and that's not so easy these days with ferreting going out the way it is. So tha keeps going until tha gets to the top of the hill which is the same one I were rolled down once for a competition and I got so giddy with being rolled that when I tried to stand up I just stumbled about and then fell in the stream. Tha could lay down here and have a sleep if tha wanted but th'art now within striking distance of the Blackbird Tavern, which is just the other side of the hill, and so I'd go on if I were thee. Once tha gets there, tha might have someone with thee what would buy thee a pint and perhaps then someone else will. Tha might even have a few bob to stand a round on tha own. So then with three pints inside thee, tha probably won't feel much like walking and so when tha gets to the edge of the wood beyond the

tavern tha could look at thy new waterproof watch and say 'Hey up, it's time for lunch'. Then all of thee go back to the tavern and eat some cheese rolls and have another pint or two. And so the afternoon just kind of shrinks away and when tha leaves the tavern all tha really wants to do is have a nap against a grassy bank. I've marked a good grassy bank on the map. When tha wakes up tha might feel like one for the road and tha goes back to the tavern if any of thee have got any brass left. Then it's probably got so late tha decides to turn round and go back and have tea at Syd and Ivy's. So that's my favourite walk and I guarantee tha'll have a really good time if tha does it.

127

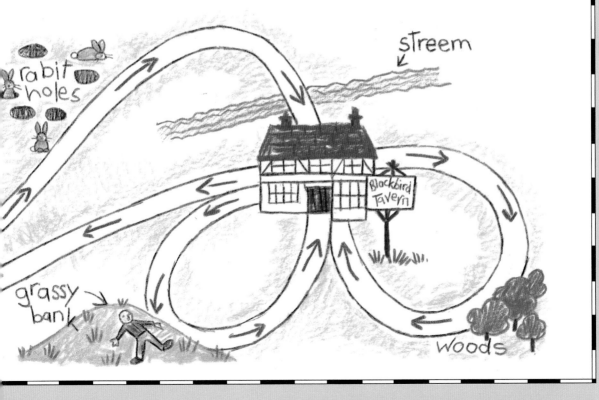